Hadfield Cawkwell Davidson
+ Partners

Architects
Engineers
Planning Consultants

17 Broomgrove Road   Sheffield   S10 2LZ

Report 139   1995

Water-Resisting
Basement Construction
– A Guide –

Safeguarding New and Existing
Basements against Water and Dampness

CONSTRUCTION INDUSTRY RESEARCH AND INFORMATION ASSOCIATION
6 Storey's Gate London SW1P 3AU
E-mail switchboard@ciria.org.uk
Tel: (0171) 222 8891   Fax: (0171) 222 1708

Summary

The report is presented in two parts; a summary report and the full report, with detailed guidance. The full report sets out to update CIRIA Guide 5 (published in February 1978). In fulfilment of its brief it:

■ gives additional guidance on water and vapour protection of new and existing basements;

■ distinguishes between guidance appropriate to deep (commercial) and shallow (residential and non-residential) basements;

■ includes reference to forms of deep basement construction such as diaphragm and secant walls, contiguous bored piles and shallow basements of concrete, masonry or steel sheet piling;

■ provides illustrative examples of construction types;

■ takes account of the control of dampness by appropriate ventilation (including air conditioning) and heating.

The report contains some generalisations. These must not be seen as restricting the designer or preventing him from selecting the precautions best suited to the use specified by the client, for new or existing basements. It should not therefore be used to justify criticism of existing designs.

It is primarily intended for use by architects, engineers, surveyors, contractors and their clients. It should also assist students and trainees in most disciplines of the construction industry.

The report takes particular account of BS8102: 1990, the Building Regulations 1991, and the work of the Institution of Structural Engineers' Committee on Deep Basements, which provided authoritative information at the time of the research.

The design of basements requires consideration of such a large number of factors that specific recommendations are not appropriate and would not necessarily cover all cases. The following points should be considered:

1. The report concentrates on the parameters of water-resisting design, giving generalised solutions as examples.

2. Each design needs to be tailored to the particular circumstances.

3. Detailed recommendations cannot be specifically related to grades of use.

4. The water-resisting performance of a basement construction is only one contribution to the control of the basement environment.

5. Systems consisting of a combination of passive and active precautions form the basis of control of the internal environment.

6. Guidance is not given for basements to be used for cold stores or food processing where special design factors and additional health regulations may apply.

7. To minimise the risk of disputes arising, it is in the interests of owners, designers and contractors to clarify local regulatory requirements. They should also agree the acceptance criteria for the internal environment, for basements under construction or being upgraded, and the time, after completion, when they should be applied.

Reference to recommendations in BSI Codes and Standards applies to the contents at the time this guide was prepared; those using the guide should always refer to the latest edition of the Code or Standard, including all amendments.

The research culminating in this report was carried out for CIRIA by Mott MacDonald, Special Services Division, St Anne House, 20-26 Wellesley Road, Croydon CR9 2UL.

Water-Resisting Basement Construction — A Guide —
Safeguarding New and Existing Basements against Water and Dampness
Construction Industry Research Information Association
Report 139, 1995

© CIRIA 1995
ISBN 0 86017 4268
ISSN 0305 408X
Thomas Telford ISBN 07277 2042-2

Keywords	Reader interest	Classification	
Basements, Construction Methods, Water-resistance, Integral Protection, Tanking Protection, Drained Cavity Protection, Monolithic Boxes, Piled Walling, Waterstops, Joint-Fillers, Sealants, Condesation, Moisture, Vapour Heating, Ventilation Repairs	Clients, Architects, Engineers, Contractors, House Builders, Building Services Designer, Building Materials Suppliers, Regulatory and Advisory Bodies, Building Surveyors, Building Construction Students	AVAILABILITY	Unrestricted
		CONTENT	Report
		STATUS	Committee guided
		USER	Construction professionals

Foreword

This report was prepared for CIRIA by Mott MacDonald, Special Services Division. The research team comprised:

R.A. Johnson, C.Eng, MIStructE   (Project Director)
D.S. Leek, BSc, MSc, C.Eng, MIM, C.Geol, FGS, MICorr   (Project Manager)
M.P. Cope, BSc, MSc, FGS   (Project Engineer - Materials)

With contributions from:

S.M. Davies, BSc, C.Eng, MICE   (Project Engineer - Construction)
E.S. King, BSc, DiplEng, MPhil, C.Eng, MICE   (Principal Engineer)
M.N. Edward, BEng, IPENZ   (Building Services Engineer)
J.G.M. Wood, BSc, PhD, C.Eng, MICE, FIStructE, FIAgrE   (Consultant)

The research was assisted with both information and comment by a project steering group consisting of:

Mr D. Shaw **(Chairman)**	T.P. Bennett Partnership
Mr M.F. Atkinson	National House Building Council (N.E.)
Mr A. Bhogal/Mr S.P. Marchand	Costain Civil Engineering Ltd
Mr R.L. Bonafont	Tarmac Industrial Products Ltd
Mr R.H. Courtier	WS Atkins Consultants Ltd
Mr G. Dean	Volclay Ltd
Mr J. Evans	Evans and Langford
Mr J.D. Findlay	Stent Foundations Ltd
Mr D. Grayson	D. Anderson Ltd
Mr R.F. Hodkinson/Mr L.R. Hancock	Taywood Engineering Ltd
Mr M. Lenaghan	Servicised Ltd
Mr M. Mutimer/Mr P. Hall/Mr P. Hayler	Sika Ltd
Mr R. Millard	Booth Engineering Services Ltd
Mr E.A. Norris/Mr A.J. Parker	Sika Contracts Ltd
Mr W.S. Paterson/Mr I.A.L.Brixey	Laing Technology Group Ltd
Mr A.J. Powderham	Mott MacDonald Group Ltd
Mr A.K. Tovey	British Cement Association
Mr D. Trowman	R.M. Douglas
Mr T. Wilkins/Mr I.Moffat	Fosroc/Expandite Ltd
Mr D. Wood	Henry Boot Southern Ltd
Mr R.B. Woodd/Mr M.D. Daniels	Sir Robert McAlpine Design Group
Mr P. Woodhead	Department of the Environment
Mr P. Wright/Mr D. Richardson	Bovis Construction Ltd
Mr E. Dore **(Research Manager)**	CIRIA

Funds to carry out this work were provided by:

Booth Engineering Services Ltd
Bovis Construction Ltd
CIRIA
Costain Group Ltd
D. Anderson & Son Ltd
Department of the Environment
Evans and Langford
Fosroc Expandite Ltd
Henry Boot Southern Ltd
Laing Technology Group Ltd
Mott MacDonald Group Ltd
National House Building Council
R.M. Douglas
Servicised Ltd
Sika Contracts Ltd
Sika Ltd
Sir Robert McAlpine Design Group Ltd
Stent Foundations Ltd
Tarmac Industrial Products Ltd
Taywood Engineering Ltd
T.P. Bennett Partnership
Volclay Ltd

Acknowledgements

The Research Team also wish to acknowledge the information, comments and assistance received from many others including:

Mr M. Beyer	Bauer Foundations
Mr C. Burdett	British Cement Association
Mr G. McShane	British Steel Corporation
Mr A. Aldred	Cementaid (Europe) Ltd
Mr P. Willcocks	Department of the Environment
Mr G. Dickinson	Evans and Langford
Mr R.W. Turner/Mr D.A. Pattinson/	
Mr A. Brown/Mr M.P. O'Connell	Mott MacDonald Group Ltd
Mr R. Dixon	PSA
Mr A. Clutterbuck/Mr R. Newlyn	Renlon
Mr C. Buss/Mr J.G. Critchley	Servicised Ltd
Mr A.S. Marco	Try Group Services Ltd
Mr A.G. Peters	Wates Construction (London) Ltd
Mr R. Noble	Booth Engineering Services Ltd

Extracts from British Standards are reproduced with the permission of BSI. Complete copies can be obtained from BSI Customer Services, 389 Chiswick High Road, London, W4 4AL, Tel. 0181 996 7000.

Contents

List of Figures

List of Tables

1   Introduction and definitions

Basements can provide space for most commercial activities, storage or car parking. In residential applications they provide valuable additional space, which can be efficiently heated and is particularly appropriate for games rooms, storage, laundry areas and parking, without increasing the height of the building.

Extracts from this report are contained in a summary report which highlights the principles governing decision-making at the early design stage. The summary report identifies factors that most concern those making preliminary project appraisals for new basements or remedial or improvement work to existing basements. Both reports provide a flowchart of the design process (given in Chapter 3 as Figure 3.1).

The full report, with more comprehensive and detailed guidance, provides a replacement for the existing CIRIA Guide 5, in the light of technical developments since that guide was published in 1978. Both the full and summary reports are intended to inform architects, engineers, surveyors, contractors and their clients.

Basement design involves the selection of combinations of construction and environmental control systems that, together, provide the necessary control of the external environment to enable the required internal environment to be achieved. Imprecise criteria for environmental control have frequently been adopted in previous basement design and construction. In such cases, the guidance in this report cannot be regarded as justification for criticism of such design or construction.

Each design needs to be tailored to the particular circumstances. The choice of any particular method of achieving the required internal environment for a new or existing basement therefore remains the responsibility of the designer, who should not be restricted from using any method or system to achieve his clients requirements.

The report assumes that there will be a clear definition of the internal environment required. Furthermore, it is recommended that the basement designer should have a formal agreement defining the present or likely future needs of his client or his client's tenant and their expectations for the effectiveness of internal environmental control. On completion of the design, this agreement should be supplemented by a description of the total environmental control system, including both construction and building services contributions, their acceptance criteria, reliability and maintenance requirements.

The traditional expressions 'waterproof' and 'vapour-proof' imply construction impenetrable to both water and vapour. No matter how carefully a basement is designed and detailed, nor how high the expected standard of workmanship, there remains a possibility that it may not be 'waterproof' or 'vapour-proof' in these absolute terms. In many cases basements would not need to be so. Despite careful design, small areas of minor leakage may appear during the construction and fitting-out periods. If these are unacceptable, it would be appropriate to consider the remedial methods outlined in this report.

1.1   BASIS FOR GUIDANCE

The 1978 CIRIA Guide 5, *Guide to the Design of Waterproof Basements*, required updating and extending owing to technical developments in both design and construction methods, new materials becoming available, and recent extensive revisions to other relevant publications. This new Report is intended to complement the Code of Practice BS8102: 1990[1.1] and to take account of the report of the Institution of Structural Engineers' Committee on Deep Basements[1.2]. It also refers to the Building Regulations 1991[1.3] (effective from June 1992) and appropriate sections of BS8007: 1987[1.4] and BS8110: 1985[1.5].

Designers must consider the physical constraints of the site, the external environment (particularly hydrostatic pressure and soil investigation evidence), and the practical limitations and reliability of waterproofing systems, in their efforts to minimise the risk of unacceptable water or vapour penetration, while ensuring compliance with the Building Regulations[1.3].

1.2   SCOPE

The Report provides guidance on:

- the protection of both new and existing basements against water and vapour from the ground;

- the provision of active and passive precautions appropriate for both shallow and deep basements (including special consideration of shallow residential basements);

- the active and passive precautions appropriate for use with deep basement construction methods, such as diaphragm or secant walls, contiguous bored piles and steel sheet piling;

- the evaluation of external ground conditions;

- the requirements of the internal environment appropriate for specific uses;

- the water and vapour resistance of the individual elements that make up the structural envelope, termed the basic passive precautions[1.6], to achieve an appropriate degree of water and vapour resistance;

- the complementary role of active[1.6] (power operated) as well as passive measures for the effective control of the internal environment.

1.3   ORIGIN OF CLASSIFICATION OF INTERNAL ENVIRONMENT AND PROTECTION MEASURES

This report has followed the classification of water-resisting methods (Types A, B and C) and internal environments (Grades 1 to 4) adopted by BS8102: 1990[1.1] (Sections 3.2.4 and 3.3) but has named them basic utility, better utility, habitable and special respectively. The classification (types and grades) has evolved from the following three documents:

- CP 102:1973[1.7] initially identified two types of **structures** [*Type A*: structures *requiring* the protection of *an impervious membrane*, and *Type B*: structures *without a membrane*] '... *for preventing the entry of groundwater and surface water into a building from the surrounding areas*'. This report recognises these structure types identified in CP 102.

- CIRIA Guide 5 (1978)[1.8] added drained cavity (Type C) structures, although it was a solution that could be used with Type A or B. It also introduced three broad grades of performance (1 to 3) termed utility, habitable and special.

- BS8102: 1990[1.1] maintained the types (A, B and C) of protection classification and incorporated an extra, lower, grade of performance, but did not use the terms utility, habitable or special.

For the purposes of this CIRIA report on *Water-resisting basement construction*, the following terminology has been adopted: Grade 1 (basic utility), Grade 2 (better utility), Grade 3 (habitable) and Grade 4 (special), and the **protection classifications** Types A, B and C from BS8102: 1990 have been retained. Other definitions have been taken where possible from BS6100: 1984[1.9].

1.4 TERMINOLOGY AND DEFINITIONS

It has been necessary to examine the classifications above and generally to follow existing precedent except where noted. Terms are defined in the following sections.

1.4.1 Definitions: basement and internal environments

This report defines the following basement types:

Basement	The inhabited storey or storeys of a building constructed wholly or partly below ground level, exposed to soil, water and/or water vapour pressure.
Semi-basement	Single storey with only one, two or three walls fully, or partially, below ground level.
Residential basement	A shallow or semi-basement providing space, for storage and/or accommodation, associated with housing.
Shallow* basement	Not more than one storey wholly below ground level.
Deep* basement	More than one storey wholly below ground level.
Basement storey	Storey below the ground floor[1.1].
	A storey of which the floor is, at any point, more than 1.2 m below the finished surface of the ground adjacent to it[1.1].
Cellar	Basement used for storage, heating plant and for purposes other than habitation[1.1].

*   For the purposes of this report, an arbitrary distinction has been made between shallow and deep basements; this distinction has been introduced on the basis that, in general, there are different groundwater pressures and construction methods associated with shallow and deep basements.

This report refers to the categorisation of the internal environment given in BS8102: 1990 with additional terminology and descriptive examples of their uses as follows:

Internal environment	Four grades of internal environment, quoted in BS8102: 1990, are defined with respect to their intended function. Table 1 from BS8102: 1990 is reproduced in the report as Table 2.1. The internal environments are described in BS8102: 1990 by their uses as:

Grade 1 (basic utility)	'Car parking, plant rooms (excluding electrical equipment), workshops'.
Grade 2 (better utility)	'Workshops and plant rooms requiring drier environments; retail storage areas'.
Grade 3 (habitable)	'Ventilated residential and working areas including offices, restaurants etc., leisure centres'.
Grade 4 (special)	'Archives and stores requiring controlled environment'.

1.4.2 Environmental control

Environmental control systems	Precautions applied singly, or in combination, organised for the purpose of modifying the internal environment, to achieve the designed standard. Systems for environmental control may comprise both passive and active precautions.
Passive precautions	Fixed methods or materials that are used in the construction of a basement to provide varying degrees of moisture resistance to control the internal environment. They do not respond to changes in conditions. They are generally difficult, if not impossible, to replace or alter.
Active precautions	Methods, or processes, used to control the internal environment, capable of a limited range of response to variations of external conditions. Methods include pumped drainage, heating and ventilation. They require inspection, maintenance and possible replacement during the life of the structure.

Examples of purely passive methods are the protection Types A and B referred to in Figure 1.1 below.

Examples of the contribution of active methods are given in Sections 1.4, 3.8, 3.9 and 7.7. Internal pumped drainage (a component of protection Type C) and building management may be considered active systems.

(N.B. Membranes and waterstops that contain actively hydrophilic materials should not be confused with active environmental control systems as defined above).

Limited control	Provided by systems that restrict the ingress of water into a basement but do not control vapour concentration.
Complete control	Provided by systems that eliminate water penetration and control the concentration of vapour.
Reliability	The probability that a method, or material, will perform as specified for a defined period of time, under defined environmental conditions.

1.4.3 'Water-resisting' construction

The report refers to 'water-resisting' properties rather than using the terms 'waterproof' and 'watertight', which are commonly misunderstood in relation to concrete construction. 'Water-resisting' describes the range of ability to resist water but not necessarily to the degree of being impervious, or absolute in the prevention of 'water' penetration. The definitions associated with water, vapour and moisture adopted in this report are given below. The distinctions made in these definitions deal with properties that are comparative rather than absolute.

Water	Water in its liquid form.
Vapour	Water in its gaseous form.
Moisture	Water in the form of vapour as well as liquid[1.1].
Condensation	The process of forming water from its vapour when air is cooled below its dew-point.
Waterproof	Impervious to water; not permitting water to penetrate.
Watertight	Waterproof.
Water-resistant	Has a high resistance to water penetration.
Water-resistance	The extent to which a material prevents water penetration.
Vapour-proof	Impervious to water and vapour; not permitting water or vapour to penetrate.
Vapour-resistant	Excludes water and has a high resistance to vapour penetration.
Vapour-resistance	The extent to which material prevents vapour penetration.
Damp	The condition of a material with a higher water content than air dry, but not wet.
Damp-proof	Impervious to moisture; not permitting moisture to enter.
Damp-resistant	Has a high resistance to moisture penetration.
Damp-resistance	The extent to which a material prevents moisture penetration.
Damp-proof course	A layer of material used in construction to prevent the vertical migration of moisture, usually in brickwork structures (not to resist hydrostatic pressure).
Damp-proof membrane	A moisture- and water vapour-resisting material[1.1].
Low-permeability	Resistant to water penetration.
Hydrostatic head	Water pressure, expressed as an equivalent depth of water.
Air dry	When the surface humidity of a material is equal to, or less than, that of the ambient surrounding air.
Wet	The presence of water as a liquid, as saturated dampness, as a surface layer, a flow or a pool. This will usually be visible as a dark staining or a glistening when illuminated.

| *Tanking* | A water-resistant material applied to a structure. This may be external, reverse, sandwiched or internal. |

1.4.4 Protection types

The basic principles of the BS8102: 1990 protection types (Figures 5 and 6 of that Standard), are embodied in Figure 1.1, annotated to clarify the approach of this Report.

In practice the protection strategy (the use of types A, B or C) is not as simply specified as BS8102 indicates. Combinations of protection types are frequently used, e.g. drained protection including a vapour barrier, as Type C *and* Type A (referred to in this Report as Type CA). The nomenclature developed for convenience in this report indicating the position of the membrane in the protection system is as follows: external tanking, Ae; external reverse tanking, Ae$_r$; sandwiched tanking, As; internal tanking, Ai (see Figures 3.3, 3.12 and 3.14 for details of combinations of protection types).

1.5   OTHER TERMS

| *Client* | The developer, owner, occupier or other person for whom the basement is being designed and built, improved or repaired. If the client is not also to be the sole occupier of the basement, he will have contracts with the occupiers and should provide the design team with all necessary information on the current and intended occupancies. |

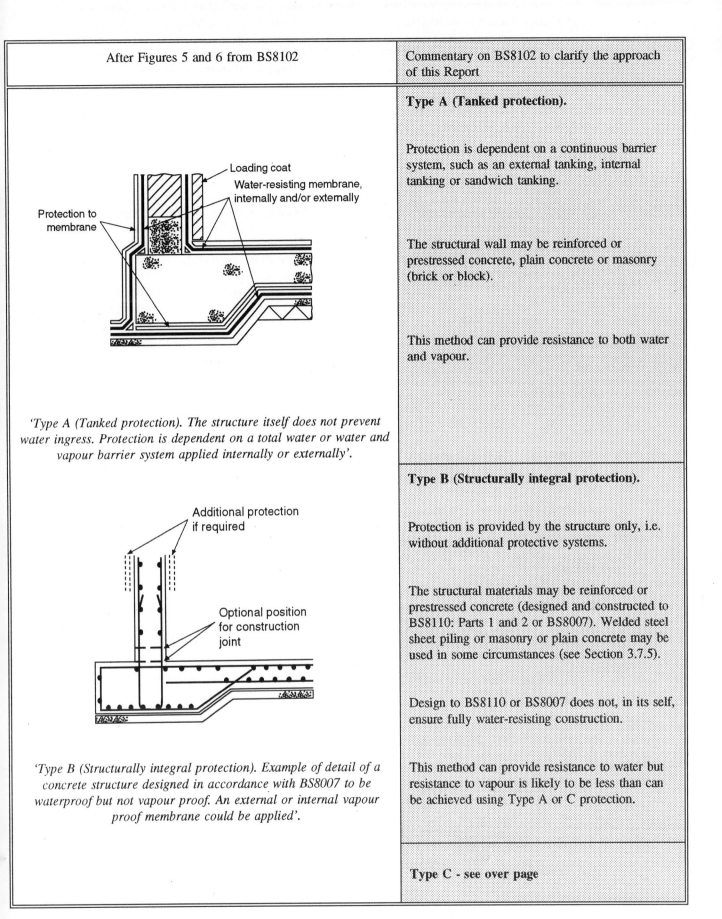

After Figures 5 and 6 from BS8102	Commentary on BS8102 to clarify the approach of this Report
	Type A (Tanked protection).
	Protection is dependent on a continuous barrier system, such as an external tanking, internal tanking or sandwich tanking.
	The structural wall may be reinforced or prestressed concrete, plain concrete or masonry (brick or block).
	This method can provide resistance to both water and vapour.
'Type A (Tanked protection). The structure itself does not prevent water ingress. Protection is dependent on a total water or water and vapour barrier system applied internally or externally'.	
	Type B (Structurally integral protection).
	Protection is provided by the structure only, i.e. without additional protective systems.
	The structural materials may be reinforced or prestressed concrete (designed and constructed to BS8110: Parts 1 and 2 or BS8007). Welded steel sheet piling or masonry or plain concrete may be used in some circumstances (see Section 3.7.5).
	Design to BS8110 or BS8007 does not, in its self, ensure fully water-resisting construction.
'Type B (Structurally integral protection). Example of detail of a concrete structure designed in accordance with BS8007 to be waterproof but not vapour proof. An external or internal vapour proof membrane could be applied'.	This method can provide resistance to water but resistance to vapour is likely to be less than can be achieved using Type A or C protection.
	Type C - see over page

Figure 1.1   Water and vapour protection following the categorisation of BS8102: 1990

The three categories shown here are the basic structure protection classifications. It should be noted that they may be used alone or in combination.

After Figures 5 and 6 from BS8102	Commentary on BS8102 to clarify the approach of this Report

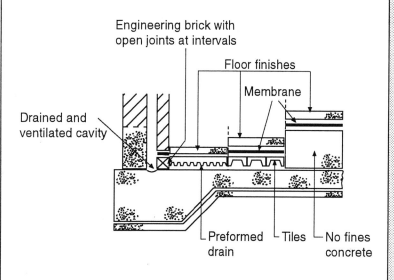

Engineering brick with open joints at intervals

Floor finishes

Membrane

Drained and ventilated cavity

Preformed drain — Tiles — No fines concrete

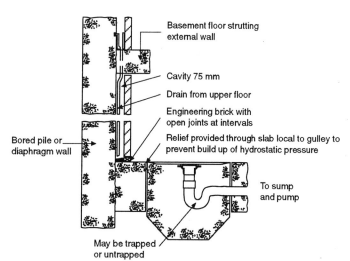

Basement floor strutting external wall

Cavity 75 mm

Drain from upper floor

Engineering brick with open joints at intervals

Bored pile or diaphragm wall

Relief provided through slab local to gulley to prevent build up of hydrostatic pressure

To sump and pump

May be trapped or untrapped

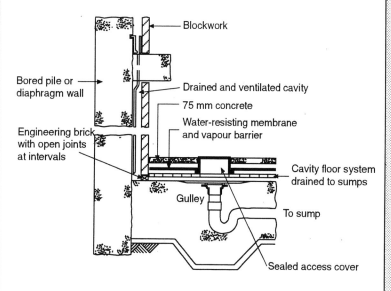

Blockwork

Bored pile or diaphragm wall

Drained and ventilated cavity

75 mm concrete

Water-resisting membrane and vapour barrier

Engineering brick with open joints at intervals

Cavity floor system drained to sumps

Gulley

To sump

Sealed access cover

'Type C (Drained protection). The drained cavity wall and floor construction provides a high level of safeguard. Provision of a ventilated cavity and horizontal damp proof membrane prevents moisture ingress'.

**Type C (Drained protection).
Shallow basements.**

Protection, additional to that from the structural envelope, is provided by means of an internal ventilated drained cavity.

The structural elements may be reinforced or prestressed concrete, plain concrete, masonry (brick or block), or steel sheet piling. [Concrete pile or diaphragm walls may also be used although these are likely to be more expensive for a shallow basement].

These precautions can provide a high degree of resistance to water and vapour ingress.

Adequate ventilation may require the provision of a low vent.

Resistance to vapour requires ventilation and drainage of the cavity and an effective damp-proof membrane over the under-drained floor.

**Type C (Drained protection).
Deep basements.**

External walls of deep basements may be constructed using diaphragm walls, secant pile walls, contiguous piles or steel sheet piling, which themselves do not give a high level of integral protection. External tanking cannot be provided in such cases.

With the addition, where necessary, of internal tanking and/or drained cavities, these construction methods can be adapted for all grades of use.

Resistance to vapour requires ventilation and drainage of the cavity and an effective damp-proof membrane over the under-drained floor.

Adequate ventilation may require the provision of a low vent.

Examples of protection are given for habitable [Grade 3] (Figures C1 and C2), and basic utility or better utility [Grade 1 or 2] (Figure C3).

N.B. Relief of hydrostatic pressure through the slab (Figure C3) may not be appropriate unless the groundwater flow is limited by low permeability ground.

Figure 1.1 continued

REFERENCES

1.1   BRITISH STANDARDS INSTITUTION
Code of practice for the protection of structures against water from the ground
BS8102: 1990

1.2   THE INSTITUTION OF STRUCTURAL ENGINEERS
Design and construction of deep basements
Institution of Structural Engineers, in preparation

1.3   HMSO
The Building Regulations 1991 (SI 1991 No. 2765 and SI 1992 No.1180) effective
from June 1992 replacing the Building Regulations 1985 (SI 1985 No. 1065).

The Building Regulations 1991, Approved Documents, especially parts:

B2/3/4	Fire spread	1992 Edition
C1/2/3/4	Site preparation and contaminants	1992 Edition
C4	Resistance to weather and ground moisture	1992 Edition
D1	Cavity insulation	1985 Edition
F1	Means of ventilation	1990 Edition
F2	Condensation	1990 Edition
H1	Sanitary pipework and drainage	1990 Edition
H3	Rainwater drainage	1990 Edition
M	Access for the disabled	1992 Edition
Amendments		1992 Edition

1.4   BRITISH STANDARDS INSTITUTION
Code of practice for design of concrete structures for retaining aqueous liquids
BS8007: 1987

1.5   BRITISH STANDARDS INSTITUTION
*Structural use of concrete. Part 1: Code of practice for design and construction, and
Part 2: Code of practice for special circumstances*
BS8110: 1985

1.6   BANHAM, R.
The architecture of the well-tempered environment
Architectural Press, 1969

1.7   BRITISH STANDARDS INSTITUTION
Code of practice for protection of buildings against water from the ground
CP 102:1973, Sections 1 and 2 superseded by BS8102: 1990

1.8   CIRIA
Guide to the design of waterproof basements
CIRIA, Guide 5, February 1978 (reprinted 1984)

1.9   BRITISH STANDARDS INSTITUTION
*British standard glossary of building and civil engineering terms, Part 1: General and
miscellaneous, Section 1.0: General*
BS6100: 1984

2 Internal and external environments

2.1 GENERAL

The designer of a basement structure must first agree with his client the required internal environment, bearing in mind all possible future uses. This internal environment may have to be achieved in the face of changing external environmental conditions during the design life of the structure. Subjective differences may occur between the client and occupier on the intended use and suitable environment of the basement. Every effort should be made to establish objective criteria.

The designer should establish, at the earliest possible time in the design process, the requirements for the environmental control system, including the active precautions likely to be required, regardless of the need for internal humidity control.

Only after a thorough review of the required internal environment and expected external conditions can methods of construction and suitable elements of the control system be assessed and basement design begin. It is most important that this review be carried out in detail, as overspecification may incur unnecessary expense and underspecification could result in expensive upgrading later, if indeed such work were to be feasible.

The control system provided to regulate the internal environmental will provide either *limited* or *complete environmental control*.

Limited control envisages the possibility of some water ingress (with no control on vapour), with the degree of ingress being project-specific and defined at the design approval stage by the specification of acceptable quantities of water and frequency of leaks. Such a definition should be quantified, within an agreed range. Once the possibility of water ingress, within quantified limits, is accepted, the system can comprise passive methods exclusively. The precautions employed must be of a high reliability, as the performance of the control system must be predictable within a range appropriate to the use.

Complete control excludes water, and the amount of vapour is controlled to achieve the minimum standards required by the Building Regulations. The client may define higher standards to suit the building function or proposed business operations. For complete control the reliability of the system should be virtually absolute. No system of passive water and vapour resistance alone is likely to achieve this level of performance; consequently complete control usually requires a combination of both passive and active precautions.

2.2 INTERNAL ENVIRONMENTS

Four grades of internal environment, with regard to basement usage and performance level, are defined in Table 1 of BS8102: 1990[2.1] (reproduced here as part of Table 2.1). This report offers additional guidance on the functional environmental requirements (relative humidity, temperature, dampness and wetness) for different uses within each grade of basement (see Section 2.2.2). Examples of the various forms of construction (passive precautions) likely to be appropriate as part of the control system, to achieve the desired internal environment, are suggested in Table 3.1 (Section 3.3).

Table 2.1   Guide to level of protection to suit basement use
(Reproduced from Table 1 of BS8102: 1990. This report adds descriptions to each grade reference and gives a commentary on the requirements in the shaded areas)

Grade of basement	Basement usage	Performance level	Form of protection*	Commentary on Table 1 of BS8102: 1990
Grade 1 (basic utility)	Car parking; plant rooms (excluding electrical equipment); workshops	Some seepage and damp patches tolerable	Type B. Reinforced concrete design in accordance with BS8110	Unless there is good ventilation, or local drainage, visible water may not be acceptable even for the suggested uses. BS8110: Part 1 contains only limited guidance on crack control and lacks consideration of early thermal movement. Using Part 1 may result in the formation of cracks with widths unacceptable in permeable ground. Additional guidance on the importance of cracks is given in Section 3.4.2. Groundwater should be checked for chemicals, which may have a deleterious effect on the structure or internal finishes. The performance level defined in BS8102 for workshops is unlikely to meet the requirements of the Building Regulations, Approved Document C for workshops, which are more likely to require a Grade 3 (habitable) environment.
Grade 2 (better utility)	Workshops and plant rooms requiring drier environment; retail storage areas	No water penetration but moisture vapour tolerable	Type A Type B. Reinforced concrete design in accordance with BS8007	Membranes may be applied in multiple layers with well-lapped joints. The performance level assumes no serious defects in workmanship, although these may be masked in dry conditions or impermeable ground. Groundwater should be checked as for Grade 1. A high level of supervision of all stages of construction is necessary.
Grade 3 (habitable)	Ventilated residential and working areas including offices, restaurants etc., leisure centres	Dry environment	Type A. Type B. With reinforced concrete design to BS8007 Type C. With wall and floor cavity and DPM	As Grade 2 In highly permeable ground multi-element systems (possibly including active precautions) will probably be necessary.
Grade 4 (special)	Archives and stores requiring controlled environment	Totally dry environment	Type A. Type B. With reinforced concrete design to BS8007 plus a vapour-proof membrane Type C. With ventilated wall cavity and vapour barrier to inner skin and floor cavity with DPM	As Grade 3

*   The 'form of protection' suitable for each grade is rigorously examined in this report and detailed guidance for concrete basements is given in Section 3.3.

2.2.1 Requirements of the Building Regulations

The internal environment must at least satisfy the performance requirements of the Building Regulations 1991. These do not define how the performance is to be quantified or the measures necessary to achieve the required environment. Measures other than those specifically referred to in the Approved Documents are permitted. However, the specific guidance given in Approved Documents C and F[2.2] relates only to Grade 3 (habitable), and possibly Grade 4 (special), environments *above drained groundwater level*. Hence, if a higher water table is present, additional precautions may be prudent. Where an external wall or floor is subject to groundwater pressure the Building Regulations refer to BS8102: 1990 for recommendations.

Clauses C1, C2 and C3 deal with site preparation, dangerous and offensive substances and subsoil drainage and are not directly concerned with the internal environment. Their application is implied by the Approved Document in the following paragraph:

'0.1 ... to reduce risks to the health and safety persons in buildings, and the stability of the building which they are in, should be safeguarded against the adverse effects of:

(a) vegetable matter, and
(b) ground water, and
(c) contaminants in or on the ground to be covered by the building.'

The means of ventilation, are covered by Clause F1, which states:

'There shall be adequate means of ventilation provided for people in the building.'

This is further qualified by performance objectives in the Approved Document by the following paragraph:

'In the Secretary of State's view the requirement of F1 will be met if ventilation is provided which under normal conditions is capable, if used, of restricting the accumulation of such moisture (which could lead to mould growth) and pollutants (originating within a building) as would otherwise become a hazard to the health of people in the building. In order to encourage its use the ventilation should not affect necessary security or comfort to a significant extent.'

The Approved Document then goes on to recommend provisions for extraction of moisture and openings for natural or mechanical ventilation. Further guidance can be found in Section 3.9.

2.2.2 Defining internal environments

The qualitative definition of the required internal environment (Grade 1 to 4) in accordance with BS8102 is essential, so that:

■   The client knows what is attainable within each grade of internal environment and the degree of control likely to be required to achieve it.

■   Those responsible for specification may quantify the objectives for moisture exclusion, although, in the absence of a reasonable prospect of compliance testing, this remains a procedure for the future.

However, it is only when the structure has reached moisture equilibrium with the external environment (which may take months, if not years) that the internal environment can be assessed to determine whether the specified environment has been achieved. Nevertheless it is desirable to establish a programme of monitoring of the internal environment in order to check for compliance with the specification. Monitoring is discussed in Section 2.2.3.

Departures from the specification may become evident during the later stages of construction, though it will not usually be possible to determine whether the final levels of dampness, relative humidity and temperature have been achieved until the building is occupied. Monitoring may therefore need to take place at specified intervals: for example, a check on water penetration before the start of decoration or fitting-out and a further check on relative humidity and dampness when the heating and ventilation are operational. However, observations after completion of the structure may be impracticable owing to the necessity for service fit-outs, decoration and a client's programme for occupation of the building. The use of de-watering during construction may delay the development of a full hydrostatic head, by which time leaks may no longer be observable.

Before finalising agreement on the required internal environment (Grade 1 to 4) the following should be considered:

- *Effects of moisture on contents and people:* items in a basement isolated from the structure may be affected by temperature, relative humidity and water. Dampness in the structure may not have a direct effect on such items, though mould and spores associated with the dampness would be unacceptable for a storage area and would preclude habitation on health grounds. The quantity of moisture held within construction materials may have a deleterious effect on the materials themselves and fittings in direct contact with them. Dampness may cause rotting of structural timber and wooden skirtings, spoil decorations and damage electrical and mechanical items.

- *Aesthetic considerations:* these may determine what is acceptable. Water dripping into a basement, or damp patches on the walls, may be unimportant if the environment is at the correct relative humidity and temperature, but may be undesirable for aesthetic reasons, except possibly in a Grade 1 environment.

The following sections identify four parameters that affect moisture levels, explain how each may be tentatively quantified, for each grade of basement, and describe the monitoring process (see Table 2.2).

2.2.2.1 Relative humidity

Relative humidity (RH) affects the degree of comfort and health of inhabitants and the life of stored items. Control is a matter of providing suitable heating and ventilation once the selected grade is achieved.

The warmer the air, the more moisture it can hold. Changes in air temperature or moisture content can cause condensation on cold surfaces. Temperature and humidity changes can occur naturally, by changes in atmospheric conditions, or artificially, by habitation or industrial processes[2.2]. Condensation can have an indirect effect on health by promoting the growth of mould and infestation by mites. Mould is always associated with pure water from condensation. This generally occurs at the bottom of walls, which may be cooler than the top or where steam may occur, e.g. in bathrooms in corners at the top. In addition, fungi may develop in wood or decorations, which may be damaged.

It is the normal function of the building services engineer to determine the relationship between relative humidity, dew-point and air temperature for a particular basement environment by the use of psychometric charts or hygrometric tables. An example of such a chart is given in BS5250: 1989[2.3].

Design of active measures for heating, ventilation, moisture transfer and condensation can then be undertaken. Their requirements are covered by Section 3.9 and Approved Document F1 of the Building Regulations[2.2].

Table 2.2   Guidance on the functional environmental requirements for basement usage

Grade of basement	Relative humidity	Temperature	Performance level	
			Dampness	**Wetness**
Grade 1 (basic utility)	>65%, normal UK external range	Car parks: atmospheric Workshops: 15~29 °C. Mechanical plantrooms: 32 °C max, at ceiling level	Visible damp patches may be acceptable	Minor seepage may be acceptable
Grade 2 (better utility)	35~50%	Retail storage: 15 °C max Electrical plantrooms: 42 °C max	No visible damp patches, construction materials to contain less than the air-dry moisture content	None acceptable
Grade 3 (habitable)	40~60% 55~60% for a restaurant in summer	Offices: 21~25 °C Residential: 18~22 °C Leisure centres: 18 °C for spectators 10 °C for squash courts 22 °C for changing rooms 24~29 °C for swimming pools Restaurants: 18~25 °C Kitchens: 29 °C max	None acceptable Active measures to control internal humidity may be necessary	
Grade 4 (special)	50% for art storage >40% for microfilms and tapes 35% for books	Art storage: 18~22 °C Book archives: 13~18 °C	Active measures to control internal humidity probably essential	
(N.B. The limits for a particular basement application should be agreed with the client and defined at the design approval stage).				

Relative humidity (and temperature) resulting from the overall nature of the structure and heating and ventilation can be measured as follows[2.4]:

- internal and external atmospheric humidity using a hygrometer
- internal and external air temperatures using a thermograph
- internal surface temperatures using a probe thermometer

2.2.2.2 Temperature

Temperature also affects the degree of comfort and health experienced by inhabitants and the life of stored items.

Temperature varies across a basement wall from the inner face, usually above dew-point, to the outer face, usually below dew-point. At some intermediate position the temperature will be equal to the dew-point and condensation will begin at this plane. This is interstitial condensation (see Section 3.9, Figure 3.20), and dampness within a wall is dependent on this effect. The effect of a thermal gradient is to concentrate moisture in the cooler section and to reduce the moisture content of the warmer section; i.e. a net movement of moisture towards the cooler section results.

Further detail concerning thermal transmittance, moisture transfer and condensation is given in Section 3.9.

2.2.2.3 Dampness

This is a function of the moisture content of a material. Every material will equilibrate with the relative humidity of the surrounding air and will either gain or lose moisture to achieve equilibrium. A material is said to be 'air-dry' if it is no longer losing moisture to the surrounding air. A material is damp if it is wetter than air-dry (see also Section 1.3).

Dampness is caused either by condensation, as described above, or by the ingress of moisture from the ground. The deleterious effects of dampness are described above for condensation. However, water from the soil is usually a dilute solution of various minerals including nitrates, chlorides, etc., which may prevent mould growth.

Moisture is contained by construction materials as:

- *Chemically combined (bound) water.*
  Excess water used in building materials (such as concrete, plaster or screed) may take up to a year to evaporate. Any remaining water will be bound and will not contribute to dampness.

- *Moisture absorbed from the air.*
  If the relative humidity is low then this should not be a problem unless the material contains hygroscopic salts, which may absorb water.

- *Capillary moisture migrating from the external environment.*
  Rising damp in walls moves by capillary action. Moisture enters basements owing to the porosity of concrete or masonry, through hairline cracks or as a result of local imperfections.

It is possible to measure the moisture content of a sample of a building material, although this may not be representative owing to the variability of the material and the environment within the building. Four methods of in-situ measurement are described below.

- *Sampling.*
  A destructive method, which involves measuring the moisture content or the percentage relative humidity of the sample by drying in an oven.

- *Impervious cover.*
  A transparent impervious cover is sealed onto the wall and the amount of moisture trapped on its inside surface is measured.

- *Humidity transfer.*
  A wooden patch is stuck to the surface, or a wooden plug is inserted into a hole drilled into the material. This is allowed sufficient time for the moisture content of the wood to equilibrate with that of the structure; this is then measured either by removal and oven drying or in situ with a moisture meter.

- *Moisture meters.*
  These operate on either conductance or capacitance principles and measure electrical current, which may be related to moisture content for a specified material.

Moisture meters are probably most widely used. They can be used to plot contours of moisture content over the whole of a wall or other surface.

It is possible to measure dampness in an accessible material but it is not always possible to identify the origin or the quantity of moisture.

2.2.2.4 Wetness

This may originate from condensation or from leaks through the structure.

As described in Section 2.2.2.1, condensation is a function of relative humidity and temperature, and their measurement should establish whether wetness is likely to occur as the result of condensation. The results of monitoring may not be conclusive after the event, as the internal environment may have changed.

Wetness is not usually a matter of degree. It is either acceptable (e.g. Grade 1, basic utility environment) or it is not. Water entering a habitable basement (Grade 3) is unacceptable.

Leakage water is often difficult to collect for measurement. For a comparative measure it may, if it is appreciable, be drained to a sump served by an automatic pump of known capacity; the time periods when the pump is in operation are recorded. Levels of leakage in excess of those specified (see Section 3.1) would require tracing and remedial treatment (see Chapter 5).

Excessive condensation may be the result of a design or specification fault, which could be cured by improved insulation and/or ventilation or additional heating.

2.2.3 Quantifying the required internal environment

Table 2.1 defines the internal environment in terms of performance level requirements for examples of basement usage. This section provides guidance on the quantitative values for the four parameters used to describe the internal environment. Table 2.2 summarises the recommended characteristic requirements (established in Section 2.2.2) for particular forms of basement use. Monitoring is made difficult by the dynamic nature of the internal environment. The frequency, method of testing and testing period must be agreed at the design approval stage and be clearly specified.

2.2.3.1 Grade 1: basic utility

In most instances, the functioning of mechanical plant and electrical switchgear is unaffected by slight seepage through walls and floors, provided the water does not impinge directly onto the equipment. However, a wet floor can be a hazard to maintenance staff as well as increase the rate of corrosion of steel casings and frames in contact with it. Generally, a raised working area may be desirable, and all equipment should be mounted on plinths.

It is unlikely that atmospheric moisture will affect mechanical plant unless it is continually at such a level as to cause an unreasonably fast rate of corrosion. One exception is that air compressors need to be fitted with air-driers if they are to operate in constantly damp conditions. Ferrous pipes, conduits, wall brackets and their fixings etc., will corrode if unprotected.

Damp air may cause electrical installations to malfunction. Permanently damp conditions may encourage biological degradation of plastic insulation. Ventilation of the plant space is therefore important.

Water ingress to underground car parks must similarly be controlled. Cars are likely to introduce significant amounts of water on wet days, which should be drained away. There is also the danger of corrosion and discoloration of paintwork on the cars due to seepage through the ceiling slab. This generally arises from the failure to waterproof car park floors, rather than from failure of the basement itself.

Table 2.3   Summary of environmental parameters for Grade 1 basements

---

Limits on environmental parameters for a Grade 1 basement:

Relative humidity. Items stored in such basements should not normally be unduly affected by high relative humidity. Ventilation draws air directly from the atmosphere and conditions equivalent to prevailing atmospheric, i.e. RH greater than 65% (normal UK external range), are therefore normally acceptable.

Temperature. Grade 1 basements would not normally be heated, and temperatures equivalent to prevailing atmospheric would normally be acceptable.

Dampness. The requirements for dampness will depend on whether the basement is to be decorated in any way and the sensitivity of any electrical equipment to be installed. If the basement is not to be decorated, then visible damp patches may be tolerated. A higher specification may be required if the walls are to be painted, etc. It is normally expected that the construction materials will not be wetter than 85% RH.

Wetness. Minor seepage would be acceptable through the walls and joints if the basement is not to be decorated. A typical criterion may be: traces of water visible at construction joints and cracks not closer than at, say, 6 m centres (twice storey height) and traces of water on the floor limited to a few millimetres in depth in a channel along the wall.

2.2.3.2   Grade 2: better utility

It may be desirable that boilers or other heat-producing equipment be excluded from basements to avoid excessive drying of the construction materials, which may result in rapid degradation or shrinkage. Where this is considered to be a serious problem, and such use is unavoidable, the equipment should be effectively heat-shielded from the structure. Insulation of the walls will have little effect where the conditions are not in equilibrium (e.g. a continuous heat source) although there may be a local benefit in protection from radiated heat.

Table 2.4   Summary of environmental parameters for Grade 2 basements

---

Limits on environmental parameters for a Grade 2 basement:

Relative humidity. RH should be controlled by heating and ventilation to be in the range 35~50%.

Temperature. Grade 2 basements should be controlled by heating and/or cooling to be in the range 15~42 °C.

Dampness. There should be no visible damp patches: i.e. materials should have less than the air-dry moisture content. There would usually be some form of decoration on the internal surfaces, which should be tolerant of this level of moisture.

Wetness. None acceptable.

2.2.3.3 Grade 3: habitable

No visible penetration of water is permitted and condensation should only occur in exceptional circumstances. Basements are required to be suitable for human occupation as offices, workshops or residential accommodation. Care should be taken to choose decorative finishes that are both suitable to the occupation and compatible with the environmental control system.

The Building Regulations Approved Document (discussed in Section 2.2.1) specifies the conditions of rooms for human habitation. However, the Building Regulations 1991[2.2] and the Building (Inner London) Regulations 1985[2.5] requirements are limited to:

> 'ensuring that floors next to the ground, walls and roof are not damaged by moisture from the ground, rain or snow and do not carry that moisture to any part of the building which it would damage.
>
> Damage can be avoided either by preventing moisture from getting to materials which would be damaged or by using materials which will not be damaged.'

The minimum ventilation requirements of the Building Regulations (Approved Document F1[2.2]) for inhabited rooms should be sufficient to keep the relative humidity of the air in the acceptable range and may remove, by evaporation, any dampness resulting from vapour penetration. If they do not, then increased (mechanical) ventilation (active control measures) may be required.

Table 2.5   Summary of environmental parameters for Grade 3 basements

---

Limits on environmental parameters for a Grade 3 basement:

Relative humidity. Ventilation, heating and air-conditioning should provide typical levels in the range 40~60%. Generally mould spore germination will be prevented provided the RH is kept below 70%.

Temperature. Building usage will determine target temperature. Typical values would be in the range 21~25 °C for offices and in the range 18~22 °C for leisure centres.

Dampness. All materials at the surface of the finished interior should be air-dry. Air-dry in this case assumes an indoor inhabited environment with an RH not exceeding approximately 70%.

Wetness. None acceptable.

2.2.3.4 Grade 4: special

Complete environmental control is essential, as condensation can be disastrous for Grade 4 basements, and active measures for ventilation, heating or full air-conditioning of the basement become essential. Ventilation alone cannot be relied upon to remove humidity caused by water penetration; hence the design must also aim at the highest possible degree of moisture exclusion using passive methods.

The penetration of water or water vapour must therefore be reliably controlled within this grade. The most stringent requirements are imposed because of the susceptibility of the contents to deterioration by moisture. Typical environments are controlled with air-conditioning, with very little incidental natural ventilation likely.

Where it is essential to use a basement for sensitive storage purposes, a satisfactory solution demands very careful liaison between all parties responsible for the design, particularly the structural engineer, the building services engineer and the specialist advising on the operational requirements of the archive or store.

Table 2.6   Summary of environmental parameters for Grade 4 basements

Limits on environmental parameters for a Grade 4 basement:

Relative humidity. The range of permitted relative humidity should be agreed with the user. It is likely that active heating and ventilation will be required to sustain typical levels of 50% for art storage, 40%-50% for microfilm and tapes and 35% for books.

Temperature. The range of temperature will vary depending on the basement use but should be tightly specified, typical values would be in the ranges 18°C to 22°C, for art storage, and 13°C to 18°C, for the storage of books.

Dampness. All materials at the surface of the finished interior should remain air-dry. Air-dry in this case assumes an indoor environment with an RH in the range 35% to 50% (dependent on the use).

Wetness. None acceptable.

2.2.4 Monitoring internal environment

It may not be possible to construct an underground structure with the required water resistance without remedial works, even when all reasonable precautions have been taken. Defective work may not be immediately apparent, and leaks may occur well after construction has been completed owing to changing external environmental conditions, e.g. rising groundwater, the sump effect of the excavation, differential settlement, etc. The aim of monitoring must therefore be to locate leaks at the earliest possible opportunity, so that remedial works may be undertaken to ensure that the basement has the specified water-resistance at handover. Thereafter, further monitoring may be required and, if external conditions change, further work may be necessary.

The criteria given in Section 2.2.3 may be used to check the basement environment after construction, using a combination of visual examination and measurements of temperature, RH and moisture content. To detect changes that occur during and after construction, measurements will be required to be taken at several stages, as follows.

2.2.4.1 Measurements taken immediately after completion of basement construction

Serious departures from the specification, such as leakage in Grade 3 or 4 environments, may become evident at, or before, this stage. However, it will not be possible to determine whether the specified levels of dampness and/or relative humidity control have been achieved until the construction materials have reached equilibrium, generally after the basement has been occupied, or is in use. The investigation of leaks may need to be delayed until long after de-watering, if used during the construction, has stopped. If internal lining walls have been constructed, early leaks may not be detected easily without specifically inspecting cavity drains, unless the leaks are sufficiently serious to show at the foot of the wall.

2.2.4.2 Measurements taken after completion of the building

While being fitted out the building may have been decorated but not subjected to service conditions: e.g. not fully heated. Departures from the specification that cause spoiling of the decorations or noticeable damp patches can be remedied (see Chapter 5). If the internal environment has been tightly specified then monitoring of the environmental control systems should take place to ensure and maintain compliance with the specification.

Measurements in unoccupied buildings for Grades 3 and 4 are almost valueless. Measurements in occupied dwellings should be made during cold weather, with normal occupancy and with heating and ventilation systems operating (the maximum thermal gradient is achieved), to ensure that the maximum levels of dampness and relative humidity are measured. The maintenance period should be at least one year to allow the full range of external environmental conditions, and equilibrium conditions of materials to be reasonably established.

2.3   EXTERNAL ENVIRONMENTS

2.3.1   Defining the external environment

Construction materials (including those used to improve the water resistance, e.g. tanking membranes) must be protected from chemical attack, and undesirable substances must be prevented from entering the basement. In particularly aggressive ground conditions the provision of an impermeable external membrane and/or ventilated cavities (including provisions for collection and venting of gases) may be necessary solely to protect the structural materials or to prevent harmful substances from entering the basement. This may influence the choice of form of construction, the passive precautions selected and materials suitable for use in the external environment. It is essential that underground structures be durable, as the opportunities for maintenance and repair are limited.

In concrete construction, suitable durability is achieved by relating concrete grade, cement content, water/cement ratio, crack widths and depth of cover to reinforcement, to the exposure conditions. Problems occur with exposed concrete underground structures when high concentrations of chlorides, sulphates or other harmful chemicals are present. In aggressive ground the need may arise for a considerably more robust damp-resisting system than would be necessary to satisfy the requirements for the control of the internal environment. Other types of materials are susceptible to attack from other chemicals: for example, bitumen-based materials may be degraded by organic solvents.

The maximum possible amount of information on all aspects of the site should be collected. This should include geology (on both a regional and site-specific scale) and geotechnical properties of the soil, history and topography of the site, groundwater conditions and general site information. Sampling should include groundwater (for chemical analysis) and disturbed and undisturbed soil samples (for chemical analysis and material properties). Much of the information collected will be needed for planning the construction process, determining soil loads, predicting the interaction of ground and structure and proceeding with structure design[2.6]. Such information will influence the approach to design of the protective system and the selection of materials.

The following sections describe the requirements of the Building Regulations and the effects of the external environment in terms of groundwater pressures, sulphate and chloride concentrations, ground acidity, bacteriological presence, contamination and gases on construction materials. Limits for the classification of the external environment for each of these parameters are suggested in Table 2.7.

2.3.2   Requirements of the Building Regulations

Approved Document C, clauses C 1/2/3[2.2], covers site preparation, dangerous and offensive substances and subsoil drainage. They define a contaminant as:

'*0.2 Contaminant means any material in or on the ground to be covered by the building (including faecal or animal matter) and any substance which is or could become toxic, corrosive, explosive, flammable or radioactive and so likely to be in danger to health or safety.*'

Table 2.7   Classification of external environment

Classification of external environment	Hydrostatic pressure (m)	Sulphate concentration (SO$_4$)[2.10] — Total acid soluble SO$_4$ (%) in soil or fill	2:1 Water/soil extract (g/l)	Ground-water (g/l)	Chloride concentration in groundwater (mg/l)	Acidic ground (pH)[2.10]	Measures to be considered[1] — Hydrostatic pressure	Sulphate concentration	Chloride concentration (reinforced concrete only)	Acidic ground
Mild	< 1	< 0.24	< 1.2	< 0.4	0–2000	> 5.5	Normal good practice applies			
Moderate	> 1 < 5	If > 0.24 classify on basis of 2:1 water/soil extraction	1.2–3.7	0.4–3.0	2000–5000		Where hydrostatic pressure greater than five times the thickness of the concrete, advance classification of external environment by one class[2.10]	SRPC[2] or combinations of Portland cement plus either pfa or ggbs concrete[3]. SRPC mortar must be used in brickwork	'Good' quality Portland cement or Portland cement plus either pfa or ggbs concrete with a maximum free w/c ratio of 0.5	Advance classification of external environment by one class where groundwater is mobile[2.10]
Severe	> 5 < 10		3.7–6.7	3.0–6.0	5000–10 000 ——— 10 000–20 000	3.5–5.5		SRPC or combinations of Portland cement plus either pfa or ggbs concrete[2] Tanking to be applied to brickwork	Low permeability Portland cement plus either pfa or ggbs concrete, with a maximum free w/c ratio of 0.45[4] Very low permeability Portland cement plus either pfa or ggbs concrete with a maximum free w/c ratio of 0.40[4,5] Reinforcement may require additional protection	
Extreme	> 10		> 6.7	> 6.0	> 20 000 (generally not applicable)	< 3.5		As severe plus tanking	As severe plus additional protection for the reinforcement	Advance other categories by one class for static or mobile groundwater[2.10]
Other					e.g. Contamination, gases, etc.		Where any of these features are found to be present, specialist advice should be obtained			

Notes:
1. The measures to be considered when classifying the external environment should be based on an assessment of the worst case parameter, i.e. whichever of the four parameters gives the highest severity environment.
2. See BRE Digest 363 for detailed recommendations on cement types, contents w/c ratio and where Mg is present.
3. Where chlorides and sulphates coexist SRPC should not be used in reinforced concrete.
4. BS8110 gives additional advice on cementitious content and cover to reinforcement.
5. BS6349 gives additional mix design advice for structures in high chloride (marine) environments.

The hazards identified in the ground are:

- Gases (methane, hydrogen sulphide, radon and carbon dioxide)
- Solids and liquids (hydrocarbons, solvents, phenols, inert refuse containing gypsum, domestic and industrial wastes, acids, etc.)
- Combustible materials
- Radioactive materials
- Materials attacking the building fabric.

Table 2, in Approved Document C, gives advice on how to deal with selected contaminants. The regulations generally assume that the building will not be extending far below the ground surface and that construction will be in open excavation. Actions recommended are either none, removal of the hazard, in-situ treatment of the ground or filling or sealing the site.

They recognise the effect of ground conditions on measures to protect the internal environment as follows:

'In the Secretary of State's view the requirements of C1, C2 & C3 will be met by taking precautions to reduce risks to the health and safety of persons in buildings by safeguarding them and the buildings against the adverse effects of:

> *a. vegetable matter, and*
> *b. contaminants on or in the ground to be covered by the building, and*
> *c. groundwater'.*

The requirements of the Building Regulations are therefore only a starting point for the design criteria, which relate to both internal and external environments.

2.3.3 Classification of the external environment

2.3.3.1 Groundwater

Hydrostatic pressure and groundwater flow (in permeable soil) affect structural loading, buoyancy forces and may increase the aggressiveness of the external environment, which will influence the environmental control system, as the rate of water flow through any moisture path is determined by hydrostatic pressure. They could also accelerate the ingress of deleterious chemicals into the concrete so that, where these are present, a higher degree of protection will be required. A dry site is less likely to give rise to any significant chemical attack.

In the absence of site-specific data, Section 3.4 of BS8102: 1990[2.1] recommends that when assessing the overall stability and stresses on the structure, the following groundwater levels should be considered:

Basement depth	*Water table level*
0.00~1.33 m	1.00 m above base level
1.33~4.00 m	one-quarter of the basement depth below ground level
exceeds 4.00 m	1.00 m below ground level

The actual groundwater levels, as shown by site investigation, are likely to differ from the above (higher or lower), and both the predicted and measured groundwater levels should be used for design of the environmental control system. Ground of relatively low permeability, such as clay, will often provide sufficient inherent control of water such that basement structures are subjected to full hydrostatic loading conditions only in exceptional circumstances. Highly permeable ground, such as gravel, can be expected to provide 'worst case' conditions frequently and for sustained periods. However, the stability and stresses on the structure should be calculated for the worst case. The likely changes in the external environment throughout the life of the basement should also be considered.

The consequences of hydrostatic pressure could be assessed in terms of a hydrostatic pressure/wall thickness ratio. A thinner wall of a given permeability would present less resistance to moisture penetration (see Section 7.2.1). However, this ratio is automatically controlled for structural reasons (the greater the pressure, the thicker the wall: see Section 3.7.2). Further research is required to establish whether there should be a minimum wall thickness for a concrete with a given permeability and a given hydrostatic head.

Specialist advice on external ground conditions should be sought, prior to commencing design, to identify any factors that may limit construction methods, and affect durability of structural materials and/or the health and safety of persons inside. Groundwater (direction and rate) flow should be determined if possible. Moving water is preferable as it will discourage insoluble salts from accumulating on the surface of exposed concrete; however, it will increase abrasion, decrease acid resistance and may carry contaminants from adjacent ground. Free water, even if nominally static, will generally be subject to some movement if only due to convection currents.

Prior to construction, groundwater levels should be monitored over as long a period as possible in one or more standpipes or with piezometers in boreholes. It is important to establish the highest level to which the groundwater can rise, either from the standpipe recordings or from the results of local enquiry. Details of standpipes, piezometers and their methods of installation are given in BS5930[2.6]. Note, however, that basements can be subjected to external groundwater, even in the apparent absence of groundwater prior to construction. This could occur when a basement excavation forms a 'sump' in an impermeable stratum and surface water run-off accumulates around the basement. In granular soils, this may create a subterranean drain leading to a build-up of water. The effect of damage to services during construction in the proximity of the site and the likelihood of increased water levels arising in the future, on surrounding buildings should be considered within a sufficiently large radius (possibly up to 1.5 km).

It has been reported[2.7] that during the last two centuries pumping from the deep aquifer beneath London has lowered the groundwater level by as much as 70 m. Owing to the cessation of extraction, the water level is now rising, in some areas, by as much as 1 m per year. If this were to continue for 20–30 years the water pressures in the sands and clays above the chalk would increase, causing movements in the clays. These movements and the increase in water pressure could cause structural damage to some large buildings in Central London and would also increase the likelihood of leakage into basements. Any likely future rise in the groundwater level should therefore be taken into account in basement design. More extensive advice is given in Appendix A.

Sampling groundwater must be undertaken with care. It is essential that the sample is not diluted by rainwater or water used to assist drilling. If sampling is undertaken during periods of heavy rainfall the concentrations measured may not be representative of the most severe conditions. Methods for sampling and testing of groundwater (and soils) for sulphates, etc., are given in BRE IP 6/79[2.8] and BS1377: Part 3: 1975[2.9].

2.3.3.2 Sulphate concentration

Soluble sulphates in groundwater react with Portland cement to form compounds, with increased volume, causing expansion and disintegration of concrete or mortar. Progressive cracking and delamination often reduce the cementitious material to a friable or soft state. Attack continues only while there is a continuing supply of sulphates, which is dependent on the groundwater pressure and on the permeability of the soil.

Sulphates occur naturally in many soils and rock formations and in industrial wastes[2.10]. The most abundant salts are calcium, magnesium and sodium sulphate; the easily soluble sulphates such as those of magnesium, sodium, and ammonium are the most aggressive. Ammonium sulphate does not occur naturally in the ground but may be present in agricultural land where it has been used as a fertiliser. Insoluble sulphates do not readily attack concrete. Sulphates can also be present in materials such as colliery shale, which has previously (mistakenly) been used as fill beneath floors.

The sulphate content of sea water is about 2.3% total SO_3 (by mass), but the expansive compounds produced are more soluble in chloride solution and growth is inhibited. Protection against sulphate attack is not generally considered necessary in marine conditions (protection of reinforcement or exposed steel from chlorides is essential).

The likelihood of sulphate attack depends on the chemistry of the cement hydrates and the rate of moisture penetration through the concrete. Thinner unprotected structural elements, subjected to high hydrostatic pressure, deteriorate faster. Concrete and mortars must be dense and well compacted. The classification of 'aggressivity' of sulphates in the external environment for sulphates is given in Table 2.7 (the values quoted are based on BRE Digest 363[2.10], which also recognises the importance of magnesium and gives additional advice on concrete mix design to resist sulphate attack).

2.3.3.3 Chloride concentrations

Plain concrete and mortar are not affected by chlorides. Reinforced concrete may be affected, as chlorides cause and accelerate corrosion of the steel reinforcement, which leads to disruption of the concrete through expansion of the corrosion products. Chlorides can also cause non-expansive corrosion in oxygen-deficient environments through potentially more serious pitting corrosion. Chlorides are hygroscopic and deliquescent and their main effect when deposited by evaporation is to leave a permanently damp layer on the wall, which will remain after penetrating damp has been halted and the structure has dried out.

Chlorides in the ground generally originate from sea water or from sea-dredged landfill. Otherwise, the occurrence of chlorides is usually associated with that of sulphates, which may be more readily assessed by one of the appropriate methods described in Section 2.3.3.1.

Chloride concentrations should be determined by chemical analysis of soil and groundwater samples. The likelihood of chloride attack on the reinforcement, however, depends on the rate of chloride penetration into the concrete. As with sulphates, the rate of penetration can be reduced by the use of dense, well-compacted concrete. In practice, where serious chloride attack of reinforcement is possible, it will probably be necessary to protect the concrete or reinforcement by means of an impermeable coating or membrane. The classification of 'aggressivity' of the external environment with respect to chlorides is given in Table 2.7.

Reinforcement in concrete permanently saturated in sea water is not generally subject to high rates of corrosion owing to the restricted availability of oxygen (the most aggressive environment is the sea water/air interface). Reinforcement in basement walls may be susceptible to macrocell corrosion, as oxygen would be available from the inside and chlorides from the outside, where a fluctuating water content could occur owing to variation in groundwater level.

2.3.3.4 Acidic ground

Acids dissolve the cement hydrates and limestone aggregate. The risk of attack is slight in most naturally occurring groundwaters when dense, relatively impermeable concrete or mortar is used, especially if the groundwater is static. Acids may have the same effect on some bricks. Classification of the 'aggressivity' of the ground with respect to acidity (pH) is given in Table 2.7.

Acid attack of concrete may occur in areas where groundwater and soils contain organic or mineral acids, and/or dissolved 'aggressive' carbon dioxide (pure and very soft waters will leach lime from cement hydrates, resulting in disintegration). Of the mineral acids only sulphuric is likely to be found in natural groundwaters. Such conditions are found in peaty deposits in marshes, on moors, in mountain spring and mine waters. The naturally occurring organic acids are mainly lignic or humic acids and are also found in peaty soil and water[2.11-13].

If iron sulphides are exposed to aerobic conditions they can be oxidised in the presence of water to form sulphuric acid. This reaction cannot occur below the water table. Alternate cycles of aerobic and anaerobic conditions, such as may occur in regions of water level fluctuation, may therefore in the long term give rise to the concentration of acids and sulphates in this zone.

In certain marsh peats, oxidation of pyrites or marcasite can produce free sulphuric acid. The presence of sulphuric acid in groundwater is generally indicated by pH values lower than 4.3 and a high sulphate content.

The use of super-sulphated cements (not normally available in UK) or cements with a high proportion of ground granulated blast-furnace slag (ggbs) or pulverised fuel ash (pfa) can improve the acid-resisting properties of concrete. The 'aggressivity' of acidic soils depends to some extent on the soil permeability and mobility of the groundwater, i.e. the rate of supply of acid. For very low-permeability soils a lower pH may be acceptable.

Site testing of soil for pH must be undertaken immediately after extraction of the sample, as oxidation of minerals may occur on exposure to air, leading to a marked increase in acidity. Although pH values only give an indication of the potential 'aggressivity' of groundwater due to acidity, in most cases the practising engineer will have little other information. DIN 4030[2.14] directs that lime-dissolving CO_2, ammonium and magnesium contents should also be measured.

2.3.3.5 Bacteriological presence

Certain soils contain an appreciable quantity of organic matter, e.g. clays and muds. Sulphur is an essential plant element and may be present in these soils in both organic and inorganic forms. Proteins and carbohydrates are also present within the organic materials. Bacterial action in the soil can cause serious corrosion of metals. This commonly occurs in tidal mud flats contaminated by sewage or in ground contaminated by organic refuse.

Sulphides in some clays, e.g. London clay, may be oxidised by certain forms of bacteria to generate sulphuric acid, which may attack cementitious or metallic materials. The suitability of sealants and membranes should also be considered where bacteriological activity is suspected.

Bacterial presence may be tested in specialist laboratories by exposing samples of the soil to alternating aerobic, anaerobic, warm and ferro-sulphate environments. Water samples for bacterial analysis should be taken in special sterilized containers. Soil samples for analysis must be taken using sterilized un-oiled tubes and the ends of the tubes must be wax-sealed immediately on withdrawal from the ground.

2.3.3.6 Contamination

Land may have been contaminated by tipping chemical, industrial or domestic waste or by spillage from mining, processing and manufacturing industries. Many chemicals are potentially hazardous to the materials used in construction (concrete, masonry, sealants, membranes, etc.) including mineral and organic acids, fats and oils, salts, alkalis and certain coal tar distillates. Some food processing products such as sour milk and sugar can also affect cementitious materials.

During investigation for such chemicals, usually by spot checks, on potentially contaminated land, the chief difficulty lies in identifying the full range of possible deleterious compounds from a limited number of samples, particularly as the concentrations of chemicals present can vary widely. It is important in such cases to research previous land use and obtain full records.

When chemical or industrial waste is suspected, specialist advice should be sought to conduct the investigation and to specify suitable construction or barrier materials to avoid attack.

2.3.3.7 Gases

It is essential, for reasons of health, safety and durability, to protect basements from the ingress of certain gases that occur in the ground, such as methane, radon, carbon dioxide and hydrogen sulphide.

> Methane may be generated by the anaerobic, bacterial, decomposition of certain paper/fibre board *void formers*. In addition, with the prediction of rising groundwater in the London basin in the future, the potential for emission of methane from the breakdown of large quantities of organic material exists.
>
> Where harmful gases may be present in the environment in sufficient concentration to be hazard to health, measures <u>must</u> be taken to prevent their entry into the basement, including the provision of systems for their collection and safe ventilation. Where there is a possibility of the entry of gases from any source, then the detailing of cavities, crawlways, manholes and other void spaces should introduce features to seal or ventilate them, to prevent the build-up of harmful quantities of gas.

Research is currently being undertaken by BRE and CIRIA on the problems associated with methane generation.

REFERENCES

2.1   BRITISH STANDARDS INSTITUTION
        Code of practice for protection of structures against water from the ground
        BS8102: 1990

2.2   HMSO
        The Building Regulations 1991, Approved Documents, especially parts:

B2/3/4	Fire spread	1992 Edition
C1/2/3/4	Site preparation and contaminants	1992 Edition
C4	Resistance to weather and ground moisture	1992 Edition
D1	Cavity insulation	1985 Edition
F1	Means of ventilation	1990 Edition
F2	Condensation	1990 Edition
H1	Sanitary pipework and drainage	1990 Edition
H3	Rainwater drainage	1990 Edition
M	Access for the disabled	1992 Edition
Amendments		1992 Edition

2.3   BRITISH STANDARDS INSTITUTION
        Code of practice for control of condensation in buildings
        BS5250: 1989

2.4   OXLEY, T.A. AND GOBERT, E.G.
        Dampness in buildings, diagnosis and treatment
        Butterworths, 1983

2.5   HMSO
        The Building (Inner London) Regulations 1985 [DET 4472]. Statutory Instruments, 1985 No. 1936, Building and Buildings

2.6   BRITISH STANDARDS INSTITUTION
        Code of practice for site investigation
        BS5930: 1981

2.7   SIMPSON, B., BLOWER, T., CRAIG, R.N. AND WILKINSON, W.B.
The engineering implications of rising groundwater levels in the deep aquifer beneath London
CIRIA, Special Publication 69, 1989; Executive summary also reproduced separately, 1989

2.8   BOWLEY, M.J.
Analysis of sulphate-bearing soils
Building Research Establishment IP 6/79, 1979

2.9   BRITISH STANDARDS INSTITUTION
Methods of test for soils for civil engineering purposes
BS1377: 1975

2.10   BUILDING RESEARCH ESTABLISHMENT
Sulphate and acid resistance of concrete in the ground
Building Research Establishment, Digest 363, 1991, p. 8

2.11   BARTHOLOMEW, R.F.
The protection of concrete piles in aggressive ground conditions: an international appreciation. Recent developments in the design and construction of piles
Institution of Civil Engineers, 1979, pp 131-141

2.12   GUTT, W.H.
Chemical resistance of concrete
Building Research Establishment, CP 23/77 (reprinted in Concrete Magazine, 1977, 11(5) 35-37)

2.13   HMSO
Specification for highway works
Department of Transport, 1991

2.14   DIN
Evaluation of liquids, soils and gases aggressive to concrete
DIN 4030, Nov 1969

3   Design of new basements

3.1   DESIGN OBJECTIVES

The designer should first be clearly briefed on the client's requirements for the internal environment of the basement. The client, in turn, should be advised by the designer on the reliability of the proposed solution and the cost implications of the requirements arising from the limitations of the individual elements and methods comprising the environmental control system. The costs, associated with achieving *complete* or *limited environmental control* (see Section 2.1), are proportional to the initial, maintenance and operating costs of the system, and the specified level of control should be considered.

3.1.1   System reliability

The design of the environmental control system should select the project-specific set of elements that are required to control reliably the ingress of moisture into the basement. The system should only comprise the necessary elements and no others. The reliability of the system will be dependent on the reliability of the individual elements from which it has been assembled. For each element of the proposed system the reliability of lower-bound performance level can be assessed. It is not possible to quantify accurately the reliability of some elements, particularly where the quality of workmanship during installation plays a dominant role in determining whether the element performs as expected. Hence a probabilistic approach, to determining the reliability of the system cannot be fully adopted. A simplified approach which accepts the probability of failure as one (certain) or zero (impossible) can, however, be adopted for individual elements when designing the environmental control system. The consequences of failure of a particular element can then be catered for technically (by remedial measures, see Chapter 5), operationally (by the procedures adopted for the management of the environmental control system) and financially (by estimating and making provision for any necessary costs).

Where a high level of environmental control (*complete control*) is required, and where the consequences of failure are severe, the reliability of the adopted system must be virtually absolute. This will almost certainly necessitate the adoption of a multi-phase protection strategy in order to ensure that the required environment will be achieved and maintained through the life of the structure. The achievement of *complete environmental control* will have a significant cost implication, which should be made clear to the client. Where the initial costs are required to be reduced the number of elements that make up the environmental control system may be reduced and the client may prefer to accept *limited environmental control*.

3.1.2   Complete environmental control

In circumstances where complete environmental control is required the system is likely to comprise a combination of both active and passive precautions.

The elements that may be combined to form the environmental control system comprise:

Passive precautions (see Section 1.4.2)

- External drainage
- The structural envelope (incorporating Type B protection)
- Membrane protection (external, reverse, internal, Type A protection)
- Internal drained cavities (Type C protection)
- Remedial works required to overcome defects in the other passive precautions

Active precautions (see Section 1.4.2)

- Internal drained systems (pumped)
- Environmental conditioning
- Building management and control systems

The designer responsible for the passive precautions will select, specify and ensure the performance level and standard of reliability of appropriate elements of the system in association with the building services engineer responsible for the design of active precautions, heating, ventilation and pumping to satisfy the requirements for protection and to achieve the most suitable environmental control system for the particular basement. The client, in approving such a brief, should be aware of, and accept, the cost of construction, maintenance, operation and possible replacement of parts of the system over the life of the building.

3.1.3 Limited environmental control

Where limited environmental control is agreed, the client may reduce the initial construction costs by eliminating precautions that may not be required. However, by his approval of a system of limited control, he accepts that:

1. amounts, location and frequency of potential moisture ingress, must be tolerated (within the agreed limits, see Sections 2.1 and 2.2), permanently or temporarily, in terms of the basement environment, building function or business operations,

2. the costs, direct and indirect (including disruption to user operations, relocation, loss of earnings, etc), of any essential remedial repair and maintenance will be acceptable and can be funded.

3.2 DESIGN CONSIDERATIONS

Basement design is an interactive process requiring decisions to be made relating to all the sections of this report. The flowchart in Figure 3.1, shows the relationship between the various sections of the report and the information and decisions required.

During the initial design stage, the full range of feasible basement construction methods, to suit the external conditions, should be considered. The choice of construction method and structure protection type will be fundamentally influenced by:

- the client's required internal environment in relation to the site and external soil conditions

- whether the basement can be built in an open excavation, and the available access for construction

- the basement depth, extent and volume, including the mass of the structure above it and whether it extends beyond the perimeter of the building above, i.e. it has a buried roof

- the passive precautions (structure protection type) that can be accommodated within the constraints of the site

- the extent to which active precautions for ventilation, heating and insulation inside the basement and drainage inside and outside the basement are to be used to achieve the required internal environment.

The solution should be the one that has the greatest probability of achieving the required internal environment and is also the most cost-effective.

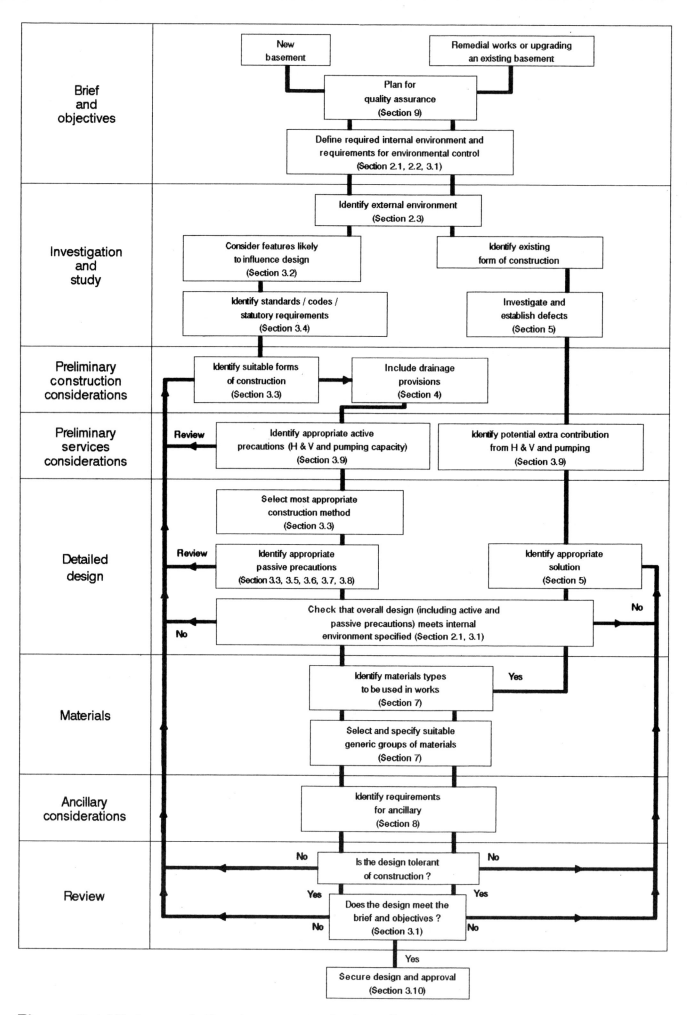

Figure 3.1 Water-resisting basement design: flowchart giving outline of method

The designer should review all the available solutions and take account of comparative costs, the usable floor areas provided, limitations on services and access restrictions, together with the following checklist of items from Clause 3.3 of BS8102, some of which reflect the fundamental restraints listed above.

(a)   *The consequences of any leakage or condensation or dampness.*

(b)   *The feasibility and form of remedial works.*

(c)   *The scope for testing during construction (e.g. the controlled application of a head of water).*

(d)   *The risk of aggressive groundwater penetrating inadequately water-tight construction and causing it damage.*

(e)   *The risk of changes to the surrounding groundwater regime.*

(f)   *The need and/or ability to incorporate movement joints within the structure.*

(g)   *The need or ability to provide heating and/or ventilation and the consequences arising in terms of humidity.*

(h)   *The need or ability to provide particular floor or wall surface treatments in response either to the users wishes or to meet some risk perceived by the designer (e.g. (a) or (g) above).*

(i)   *The impact of the chosen method of construction and the consequential risk attendant upon less than adequate workmanship.*

(j)   *The balancing of cost against risk in choosing whether further construction cost or future maintenance cost will assume priority or in choosing whether the building contract will place greater or less emphasis on a performance requirement.'*

At the preliminary design stage, the following influences on construction method, design codes, structure protection, drainage and services and maintenance costs are relevant.

3.2.1   Construction methods

This should take into consideration all appropriate construction techniques in relation to the position of walls, internal columns, movement and construction joints of superstructure, etc.

A basement should be designed in conjunction with the superstructure of the building, as the position and number of movement joints, walls and columns have a significant effect on the final cost and possibility of achieving the design objectives. This is even more important when using 'top-down' construction, which allows the superstructure to be built at the same time as the basement. The selection of basement construction method should also consider the overall mass of the structure in order to minimise potential problems from settlement and ground heave, as well as avoiding the risk of flotation, which may possibly result in the fracture of service entries.

The designer should aim to produce the simplest possible plan shape. Complicated sections in walls and slabs are difficult to form, reinforce and construct satisfactorily and often develop localised stress concentrations from shrinkage or thermal movement. Similarly, in irregularly shaped masonry walls, cracking and relative movements are greater. Emphasis should be placed on simplicity, 'buildability' and durability.

Where it is not possible to design the basement as a simple box, detailed attention must be paid to sudden changes in slab or wall direction and thickness. These cause particular problems when tanking protection is adopted (see Figure 3.2, and Section 3.6.5.2). The wall-to-floor joint is particularly prone to leakage, especially at the intersection with vertical corners (see Figures 3.3-3.5). Sealing ground slabs around pile caps requires special provisions. The use of 'buildability' aids, such as reinforcement couplers, may improve water-resistance by making it easier to prepare the joint face than where bars project or have to be bent out (see Figure 3.4).

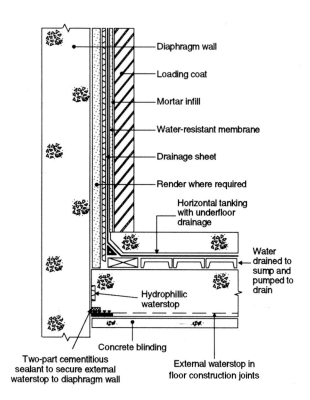

Figure 3.2 Preformed self-adhesive membrane; internal tanking with internal drainage. An example of Type A protection combined with Type C

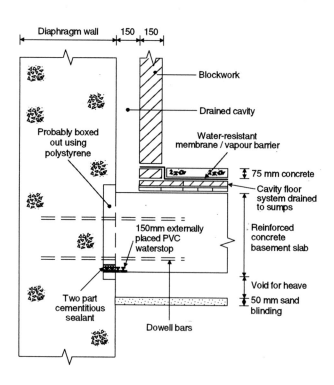

Figure 3.3 Detail of base slab / diaphragm wall junction. An example of Type C protection indicating special provisions at the wall / floor joint

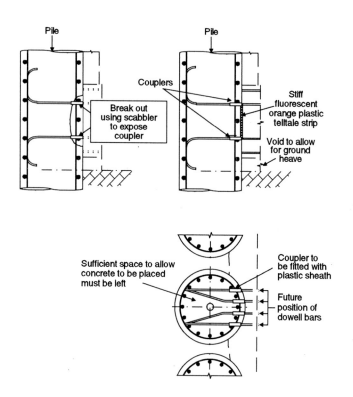

Figure 3.4 Detail of base slab / piled wall junction. A construction detail which makes it difficult to use either Type A or Type C protection

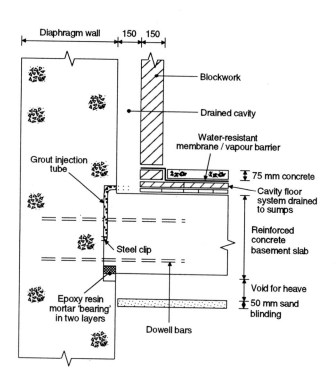

Figure 3.5 Detail of base slab / diaphragm wall junction. An example of Type C protection indicating special provisions at the wall / floor joint

3.2.2 Design codes

The guidance of relevant British Standards and Codes of Practice for durability and structural considerations, including crack width limits and the requirements of the Building Regulations (and British Standards) for materials and workmanship, fire safety, site preparation and resistance to moisture should be incorporated into the design process.

3.2.3 Structure protection

Information gained from the soil and groundwater survey (such as the presence of methane[3.1] or radon[3.2] etc.), the proximity of services and other buildings, site access and other constraints influence the design and layout of the whole building, the choice of construction methods and the elements of the environmental control system adopted.

The requirements for protection of the structural elements should be identified (i.e. tanking) and/or whether the structure requires complete or limited control to achieve the selected grade of internal environment.

The level of passive protection that may be required in typical instances of basement use is given, as a general guide, in Table 2.1. However, to provide a sound basis for client approval it will be necessary to describe, in outline, the environmental control system as a whole and the interdependence of its parts. The critical characteristics of the performance of both complete and limited control systems should be identified and quantified where possible.

3.2.4 Drainage and services

The provision of external drainage to control groundwater levels should be used wherever practical.

Active measures for heating and ventilation should be provided where complete control is considered necessary to supplement the structure protection.

Care must be taken to avoid leakage into the basement around pipes and other services that pass through the basement walls. Internal wall fixings, cable support brackets and lightning conductors must not damage the structure protection. Measures that facilitate future remedial works to seal leaks, such as the provision for post-grouting construction joints (see Figure 3.5), may also be incorporated (grout tubes should be capped to prevent a leakage path occurring prior to injection).

3.2.5 Maintenance and costs

All structures need some maintenance to achieve their design life, particularly where complete environmental control is required. Leakage into basements should be avoided by careful attention to construction details. If failure occurs, the remedial measures may be very expensive, e.g. grouting or the installation of drained cavities and drained floors.

Where pumps are required as part of the system some duplication may be worthwhile (see also Section 3.1.1) to enable equipment to be removed for regular maintenance. Equipment that runs only intermittently is more likely to break down. Typical costs of maintenance are approximately 1% of basement construction value per year.

Heating and ventilation costs will be less than for above-ground space.

3.3 CONSTRUCTION METHODS

Before suitable construction methods and materials are selected the basement should be categorised as either:

1. Deep   A basement with more than one storey, which will generally be subject to hydrostatic pressure, or

2. Shallow   A basement of one storey (including basements for residential use), which may or may not be subject to hydrostatic pressure.

This general categorisation together with the internal environment (Grades 1 to 4) enables the range of appropriate basement construction methods (and materials) to be identified. It also assists in the choice of structure protection type (A, B or C).

Table 3.1 (extending the approach of BS8102) outlines construction types and passive precautions available for different grades of internal environment in relation to deep and shallow basements, above and below groundwater level. Shallow basements, above groundwater level, often associated with residential development justify a separate more detailed categorisation (described in Chapter 6).

The principal construction materials and methods for basements are:

- concrete, plain or reinforced (precast or in-situ reinforced concrete box, diaphragm or piled walls)
- masonry
- steel sheet piling.

The appropriate use of these materials in basement construction is described in Chapter 7.

3.3.1 Deep basements

The various methods of deep basement construction, given in the report of the Institution of Structural Engineers' Committee on Deep Basements[3.3], can be summarised into the following:

- construction in open excavation
- bottom-up construction
- top-down construction.

Combinations of bottom-up and top-down systems of basement construction may be adopted.

This section describes available combinations of construction methods and examples of passive precautions for reinforced concrete deep basements subjected to a permanent hydrostatic head. The permeability of the ground will be an important factor in determining the choice of suitable construction methods. As deep basements are generally constructed using diaphragm or piled walls, it is rarely feasible to protect them with external tanking.

In general, deep basements will require a concrete structure, which will also act as a barrier to the ingress of water. Internal environment Grades 2, 3 and 4 are likely to require additional passive measures to attain the necessary resistance to moisture penetration. Internal drained cavities can normally be provided in conjunction with tanking if necessary, to achieve the highest grades.

Table 3.1   Construction methods and examples of passive precautions available to achieve the required Grade of internal environment in deep or shallow basements

Basement depth and construction materials	Target internal environment / examples of construction methods and passive precautions			
	Grade 1 (basic utility)	**Grade 2 (better utility)**	**Grade 3* (habitable)**	**Grade 4* (special)**
	Limited environmental control possibly adequate (Low cost, low reliability)		*Complete environmental control* normally required (High cost, high reliability)	
	Some water penetration acceptable	Water penetration unacceptable	Increasing requirements for vapour control	
Shallow (assumed no hydrostatic pressure, i.e. groundwater level below basement floor or drainage provided) likely to be residential **Masonry, reinforced masonry, plain or reinforced (precast or in-situ) concrete or steel sheet piling**	Grade not usually acceptable for residential basements	Masonry or plain concrete plus tanking (Type A) or drained cavity (Type C) protection ---------------- Reinforced concrete box (Type B) protection	Masonry or plain concrete plus tanking (Type A) protection and/or Type C protection ---------------- Reinforced concrete box (Type B) plus tanking vapour barrier (Type A) or drained (Type C) protection	If grade required the methods and precautions for shallow basements with permanent hydrostatic pressure should be followed
Shallow (with permanent hydrostatic pressure) **Masonry, reinforced masonry, plain or reinforced (precast or in-situ) concrete or steel sheet piling**	Masonry, plain or reinforced concrete box construction plus tanking (Type A) or drained (Type C) protection ------------ Reinforced concrete box (Type B) protection ------------ Steel sheet piling in conjunction plus drained (Type C) protection	Masonry, plain or reinforced concrete box construction plus tanking (Type A) or drained (Type C) protection ------------ Reinforced concrete box (Type B) protection	Masonry or plain concrete plus tanking (vapour barrier, Type A) *and* drained (Type C) protection ------------ Reinforced concrete box (Type B) plus tanking (vapour barrier, Type A) or drained (Type C) protection	Reinforced concrete box (Type B) with tanking (vapour barrier, Type A), plus drained (Type C) protection Passive precautions alone are not likely to be sufficient
Deep (with permanent hydrostatic pressure) **Reinforced concrete including piled or in-situ perimeter wall.**	Reinforced concrete box (Type B) protection -------------- Concrete piled wall, possibly requiring drained cavity (Type C) protection	Reinforced concrete box (Type B) protection ------------- Concrete piled wall or reinforced concrete box (Type B) plus drained (Type C) protection	Concrete piling or reinforced concrete box (Type B) plus an internal vapour barrier (Type A) or drained (Type C) protection Passive precautions alone are not likely to be sufficient	Concrete piling or reinforced concrete box (Type B) plus tanking (vapour barrier, Type A) and drained (Type C) protection Achieved only at high cost Passive precautions alone are not likely to be sufficient

Notes: When tanking is required, external or sandwich tanking systems are recommended for both new and existing basements where it is possible to use them. Such systems become feasible either by virtue of an existing permanent external surface (including faced sheet piling) or where working space is created through open excavation. The choice of tanking system also requires an assessment of the external hydrostatic pressure and its effect on the basement wall design and construction. For deeper basements, or where excavation is impracticable, internal protection by cavity construction with internal or reverse tanking may be used. This implies a reduction in usable basement volume or increased excavation volume. Integral protection must not be damaged by wall fixings. The costs of available options and associated risks will need to be evaluated. Where significant quantities of water are likely to accrue in sumps on a regular basis the drainage authority should be approached at an early stage to request acceptance of the discharge.

*   The design for Grade 3 or Grade 4 should take account of the contribution of active precautions (heating and ventilation, etc.) in achieving the required internal environment.

For more information on appropriate design standards for concrete basements, see Section 3.4.

Grade 1 (basic utility) and Grade 2 (better utility) internal environments can usually be achieved using in-situ reinforced concrete construction without any additional protection if:

- the basement foundation slab is thick, and
- maximum calculated crack widths, due to contraction and load effects, are kept to a minimum to limit excessive leakage (see Section 3.7.2.1), and
- particular care is taken with the 'floor to piled wall joints' and 'piled corners', and
- the ground is of low permeability.

Where the structural walls and floor cannot be relied upon to exclude water sufficiently, the simplest solution is to install a drained cavity. Similarly, a drained floor should be provided, which allows for an air space between the main structural slab and the floor. Any water that collects in the cavities should be drained to sumps and pumped away.

Grade 3 (habitable) and Grade 4 (special) internal environments generally require vapour control and Grade 4 may also need humidity control. Vapour can be removed by installing a naturally or mechanically ventilated drained cavity.

Deep basement construction in the form of diaphragm, contiguous or secant piled walls (which may not comply fully with the BS8007 requirements, for spacing and percentage of reinforcement for crack control) can still achieve all grades of internal environment when constructed in conjunction with additional active and passive precautions. Leak sealing/grouting can be included in the contract, or as a requirement when water levels return to normal if de-watering has been used. Further guidance on design standards for deep basements is given in Section 3.4.2.

Drained and ventilated cavity walls and floors (with the structural elements forming the primary barrier to moisture ingress) can provide a high degree of vapour control and, although not in every case essential, may be of long-term benefit where there is a risk of a future rise in groundwater level.

The passive precautions that may be used as part of the environmental control system are summarised in Table 3.2.

3.3.2 Shallow basements

This section describes the available combinations of methods for shallow basements subjected to a permanent hydrostatic pressure and constructed of:

- masonry
- concrete, plain or reinforced (precast panels or in-situ)
- steel sheet piling.

Where hydrostatic pressure is not expected, reference may be made to Section 3.3.3. Additional information on appropriate design standards for concrete basements is given in Section 3.4.2.

The measures that are likely to achieve the desired internal environment in shallow basements are similar to those summarised in Section 3.3.1 for deep basements, except that external tanking is more likely to be feasible for shallow basements. The passive precautions that may be used as part of the environmental control system are summarised in Table 3.3.

Grade 1 (basic utility) internal environment; basements for non-critical applications (e.g. car parks, insensitive storage) may be achieved, when constructed to an appropriate standard of workmanship from masonry, plain concrete, steel sheet piling or reinforced concrete 'boxes' (i.e. monolithic walls and floor continuously reinforced, in two faces, in both directions).

Alternative water and vapour control measures (and combinations) likely to achieve particular internal environments in deep basements (subject to hydrostatic pressure)

Water and vapour protection measures	Internal environment									
	Grade 1			Grade 2			Grade 3		Grade 4	
External tanking [Type A]	X			X			X		X	
Internal tanking, vapour barrier (where necessary) [Type A]	X	X	X	X	X	X	✓	✓	✓	✓
Structurally integral protection [Type B]*	✓	X	✓	✓	X	✓	X	✓	X	✓
Internal drained cavity (drained protection) [Type C]	X	✓	✓	X	✓	✓	✓	✓	✓	✓
Active precautions	X			X			✓		✓	
External drainage	X			X			X		X	

*   Design standards for concrete basements are given in Section 3.4.2.

Each column represents one possible combination of measures in the environmental control system.

Key:

X   Not usually necessary (sometimes not feasible).

✓   Precautions that may be included in the environmental control system.

Alternative water and vapour control measures (and combinations) likely to achieve particular internal environments in shallow basements (subject to hydrostatic pressure)

Water and vapour protection measures	Internal environment														
	Grade 1				Grade 2				Grade 3					Grade 4	
External tanking, vapour barrier (where necessary) [Type A]	✓	X	X	X	✓	X	X	X	✓	X	✓	X	X	✓	X
Internal tanking, vapour barrier (where necessary) [Type A]	X	✓	X	X	X	✓	X	X	X	✓	X	✓	X	X	✓
Structurally integral protection [Type B]*	X	X	✓	X	X	X	✓	X	X	X	✓	✓	✓	✓	✓
Internal drained cavity (drained protection) [Type C]	X	X	X	✓	X	X	X	✓	✓	✓	X	X		✓	✓
Active precautions	X				X				✓					✓	
Low level, below floor, external drainage (where possible and beneficial)	✓				✓				✓					✓	

*   Design standards for concrete basements are given in Section 3.4.2.

Each column represents one possible combination of measures in the environmental control system.

Key:

X   Not usually necessary (sometimes not feasible).

✓   Precautions that may be included in the environmental control system.

Grade 2 (better utility) internal environment; basements constructed as a reinforced concrete 'box', with early thermal crack control to BS8007, may be sufficiently water-resistant without any additional protective measures. For basements constructed with masonry, plain concrete or steel sheet pile walls, the provision of drained or tanked protection is likely to be necessary, where visible leakage will not be acceptable.

Grade 3 (habitable) internal environment; basements constructed from masonry, plain concrete or reinforced concrete require tanked or drained protection. Where external tanking is not possible or cannot be relied upon to give complete protection, the provision of drained protection in conjunction with a vapour barrier provides the maximum reliability against water and vapour penetration. Adequate design for heating and ventilation (active precautions) should be provided to ensure that the vapour barrier does not cause internal and/or interstitial condensation.

Grade 4 (special) internal environment; these environments are often achieved by using a reinforced concrete box structure (designed to BS8007) with vapour-resisting tanking and drained protection, together with the highest quality of workmanship. Heating and ventilation are usually essential, and relative humidity control may be required.

Piled, shallow basements are not usually economic, but using the methods described for deep basements (Sections 3.3.1 and 3.4.2) they can be designed to achieve similar standards.

3.3.3 Residential basements

A shallow residential basement may be used for storage or for habitable accommodation. Semi-basements are constructed on sloping ground. This section assumes (because of the provision of drainage or sloping ground), that such structures will not be subjected to hydrostatic pressure. If this assumption is incorrect refer to the guidance in Section 3.3.2 and Table 3.1.

The principal construction materials used in residential basements include:

- masonry (bricks or blocks)
- concrete, plain or reinforced (precast or in-situ).

Residential basements are usually Grade 3, while Grade 2 may be acceptable for utility rooms. Grade 1 is unlikely to be acceptable and Grade 4 objectives are not usually necessary.

Grade 1 (basic utility) internal environment which permits 'some seepage and damp patches' is unlikely to be acceptable even for a residential garage, although BS8102 includes parking in this grade.

Grade 2 (better utility) internal environments may be achieved using any of the protection types.

Grade 3 (habitable) internal environments will generally require some control of vapour for health reasons as well as for protection against damage through moisture ingress. To satisfy the requirements of BS8102 and the Building Regulations 1991, complete protection by a combination of methods may be necessary.

The methods of protection for residential basements are detailed in Chapter 6.

Possible passive precautions available to achieve a Grade 2 or 3 internal environment in a residential shallow basement subject to regular hydrostatic pressure are as defined in Section 3.3.2, and summarised in Table 3.3.

3.4   DESIGN STANDARDS

This section summarises the salient points from the principal British Standards concerned with the design of reinforced concrete, plain concrete or masonry basements.

A full comparison of the relevant documents is given in Appendix B and in Table B.1 for reinforced concrete basements and Table B.2 for plain concrete and masonry basements. The fundamental elements of design that are considered to affect directly the water resistance of a structure, namely materials properties, cracks, construction joints, movement joints, waterproofing treatments and drainage, are discussed below.

3.4.1   The Building Regulations (SI 1991 No. 2765)

The Building Regulations state that *'the walls, floors and roof of the building structure should adequately resist the passage of moisture to the inside of the building'*. The Building Regulations[3.4] do not deal separately with basements but treat them as part of a building.

Approved Documents[3.4] particularly relevant to basement construction include the following:

Approved Document B1 provides guidance for means of escape in case of fire, and B2/3/4 deal with fire safety and fire spread requirements generally for the above-ground storeys of buildings. However, Section 1.17 of B1 is aimed specifically at *'venting of heat and smoke from basements'*. It recognises the necessity to improve the fire safety of semi-basements by providing doors and windows on at least one external wall. In other cases, and with larger structures, more than one staircase is required for inhabited basements (Section 2.40/2.42).

Approved Documents C1/2/3 deal with site preparation, site drainage and contaminants in the ground associated with general construction practice. Approved Document C4 sets out the performance requirements in respect of a floor next to the ground which should *'prevent undue moisture from reaching the upper part of the floor'*. To achieve this level of performance, technical solutions are offered for ground-supported concrete floors not subjected to water pressure, which would therefore not be adequate for all basements. Where conditions are more onerous, the Approved Documents refer the reader to solutions from CP102: 1973[3.5] (for capillary rise of moisture) and BS8102: 1990[3.6] (for the protection of structures from water in the ground by tanking). A determination by the DoE[3.7] carries the important implication that reliance may be placed on heating and ventilation to achieve the required grade of internal environment.

3.4.2   Concrete basements to BS8110: 1985, BS8007: 1987 and BS8102: 1990

There are three codes of practice particularly relevant to the design of concrete basements, BS8110: 1985[3.8], BS8007: 1987[3.9] and BS8102: 1990. The scope of, and relationship between, these standards is discussed and a detailed comparison of their individual requirements is given in Appendix B, Table B1 (BS8004: 1986 *Code of Practice for Foundations* may also be relevant).

BS8110 states that *'water retaining structures ... are more appropriately covered by other codes'*. BS8007 *'provides recommendations for the design and construction of normal reinforced and prestressed concrete structures used for the containment or exclusion of aqueous liquids'* but *'does not cover ... the damp-proofing of basements'*. BS8102 provides *'guidance on methods of dealing with and preventing the entry of water from surrounding ground into a building below ground level'*.

Detailed guidance on crack control during the design of reinforced concrete basements, including an innovative design philosophy that overcomes this problem, is presented in Section 3.7.2.1.

3.4.3 Masonry basements to BS5628 and BS8102

Two codes of practice are relevant to masonry construction, BS5628: Part 3: 1985[3.10] and BS8102. The former gives recommendations on the prevention of moisture ingress, but not specifically for basements, while BS8102 details the requirements specific to basements.

3.4.4 Welded steel sheet piling

There are no codes that detail the requirements for welded steel sheet pile basements. There are a number of codes that give material and fabrication requirements.

Structural steel sheet piling should be a weldable, low-carbon type. In the UK, structural steel is obtained to BS4360: 1990, in which the most commonly used grades are 43 (mild) and 50 (high tensile steel). The grades are further designated by a letter (e.g. 43A, 43B) which denotes the requirements for Charpy V-notch impact testing. BS4360 also gives specific requirements for the chemical composition and mechanical properties of weather-resistant (WR50) grades rolled in the UK. The requirements for thickness are given in BS5950.

3.5 PASSIVE PRECAUTIONS (STRUCTURE PROTECTION TYPES A, B AND C)

Three forms of protection types have been illustrated and described previously in Figure 1.1, with a commentary on the information given in BS8102.

The decision on whether to rely entirely upon structurally integral protection (Type B) is crucial to basement design, and the factors which influence that decision are discussed in Chapter 2. These include:

- the degree of acceptable leakage into the basement
- durability risks from chemical deterioration of structural elements
- the risk of gas migration into the basement
- feasible methods of protection related to construction methods
- the risk of leakage associated with the protection method
- the anticipated hydrostatic pressure.

Deep basement construction is generally carried out in reinforced concrete (including piled walls). This is described more fully in Section 3.7.

Basements with buried roofs, e.g. underground car parks, etc., may require special consideration of the passive precautions to ensure compatibility with the measures adopted for the walls. Methods available for the protection of buried roofs are described in CIRIA Technical Note 145[3.11].

Table 3.1 indicates the construction method (structure and protection) likely to achieve each environment grade. It may be used, with a proposed construction method in mind, to obtain details of the passive precautions that may be required.

The required moisture penetration characteristics may not always be achieved by the passive precautions adopted, owing, for example, to construction defects. Where this is the case, recourse may be made to the remedial measures outlined in Chapter 5.

3.5.1 Water or water and vapour penetration

The internal environment grades, given in BS8102 are based upon the performance level of a protection type (A, B or C) to resist water or water and vapour penetration into the basement for particular types of usage.

The acceptable risk of moisture penetration associated with each type of structure (reinforced concrete box, piled walling, masonry, etc.) must be evaluated in view of the existing and possible future ground conditions (principally groundwater levels and type of drainage associated with soil type).

For shallow (or residential) basement construction, where there is no permanent hydrostatic head, any environment grade can be achieved utilising any of the structural materials with any of the three types of protection, although practicality and cost will vary. This is described further in Sections 3.2 and 3.3. Where slope or natural drainage do not guarantee these conditions, additional precautions may be necessary to minimise water or water and vapour penetration.

3.5.2 Aggressive ground conditions

The presence of sulphates, chlorides, acids, gases etc. in the ground and groundwater affects the durability of the structural elements below ground level (see Section 2.3).

If the risk of moisture penetration through the structural walls and floor or the likely durability of the structure or its protection is unacceptable, two options are available to achieve the specified basement internal environment:

1.   Improve the protection provided by the construction materials (i.e. by modifying the existing method and materials or by selecting an alternative method (see Section 3.5.3)).

2.   Supplement the protection provided by the structural elements (by the addition of other passive systems (see Section 3.5.4)).

3.5.3 Structures without additional protection (Type B)

Where the use of additional protection to supplement that provided by the structural elements is not feasible and/or desirable, alternative construction methods and materials may be evaluated. This may require repeating the initial design procedure outlined in Sections 3.1 and 3.2.

3.5.4 Structures requiring additional protection (Type A and C)

The protection provided by the structural elements may be supplemented principally by two methods:

1.   Tanking protection ~ external, sandwiched or internal tanking; and/or

ii)   Drained protection ~ internal drained cavity.

The main features of each protection type are defined in Chapter 1 of this report. More detailed guidance and the relative merits of the protection types are presented in subsequent sections.

Table 3.1 indicates the construction method (structure and protection) likely to be used for each environment grade. It can be used with a proposed construction method in mind to obtain details of the passive precautions that may be appropriate.

3.6 TYPE A: TANKING PROTECTION

Tanking (Type A) protection provides a continuous barrier system which excludes water and/or water vapour and may exclude gases (see Section 2.3.3.7). It can be installed:

- on the exterior face of walls and floors (external)
- onto some external source of support (reversed)
- within the construction (sandwiched), or
- on the interior face of walls (internal).

Figure 3.6 illustrates the types of tanking.

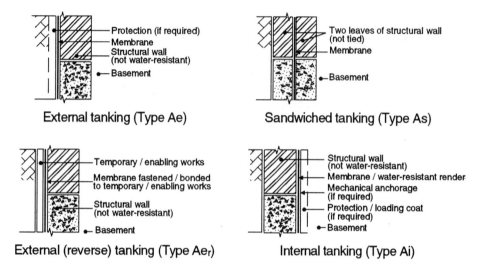

External tanking (Type Ae)

Sandwiched tanking (Type As)

External (reverse) tanking (Type Ae$_r$)

Internal tanking (Type Ai)

Figure 3.6 Tanking protection (Type A)

The reliability of tanking systems is primarily reliant on:

- the formation of adequate joints where sheet systems are used
- the prevention of damage to the membrane during construction
- achieving a satisfactory bond to the substrate.

They are not generally applied to exposed floor surfaces because they lack the necessary wearing properties and are unable to resist external hydrostatic pressure.

A tanked structure is generally required to be monolithic, with a minimum of movement (especially transverse) at joints. The tanking system should be selected to accommodate the movements that are likely to occur. For large deep basements (with a permanent hydrostatic head) tanking is only practicable with reinforced box construction, except where walls are cast onto steel piling, but may not be necessary.

For each project a full exchange of information between all the parties concerned with the design and construction of the basement and the tanking system may be beneficial. A detailed specification should be prepared, with a general arrangement and detail drawings for each section of the basement to be tanked.

The tanking system (external) should be continuous from the lowest part of the structure to at least 150 mm above finished ground level. Continuity with damp-proof courses (DPCs) or cloaking with a cavity tray are important, particularly in masonry structures.

It is important that all partition walls are also provided with DPCs at their bases, where they butt against exterior walls and around services and openings.

In masonry substructures DPCs are generally installed by the bricklayers, with dry lap joints that offer little resistance to internal water pressure. This increases the risk of leakage. DPCs should be checked to ensure that they provide continuity within a tanking system and that they can be built as detailed.

Mastic asphalt tanking details have not been included in the report but are well covered in BS8102: 1990, Section 3, BS8000: Part 4: 1989, Section 3, and the Mastic Asphalt Council & Employers Federation's, *'Tanking Handbook'*[(3.12)].

3.6.1   External tanking

The use of an external tanking system is generally preferred, if site and design conditions permit, so that external water pressure will force the membrane against the structure. Where a permanent hydrostatic head exists, the structure should be designed either to resist water penetration (Type B: structurally integral protection, see Section 3.7) or to control movement and cracking to a degree that can be reliably accommodated by the membrane. Special care should be taken where settlement of fill may occur, especially if this is used in conjunction with piling, as ground movement may rupture the membrane at vertical/horizontal interfaces. Hydrophilic membranes can be considered, as these have self-healing properties provided they have been fully hydrated and are not unduly dehydrated in service (see Section 7.3.1.3).

Figure 3.7 shows an example of this system of protection for a concrete basement. It also uses the reverse tanking derivative of this for the floor slab (see Section 3.6.2).

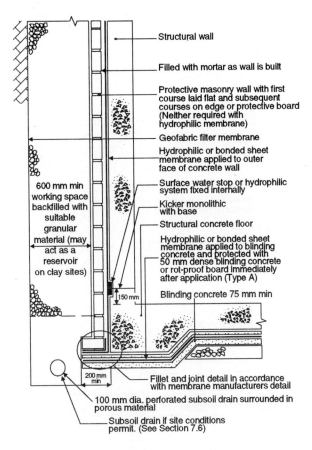

Figure 3.7 Concrete structure with external
membrane (Type Ae)

Figures 3.8 and 3.9 give examples of external tanking for a masonry basement using a sheet membrane and a hydrophilic membrane respectively.

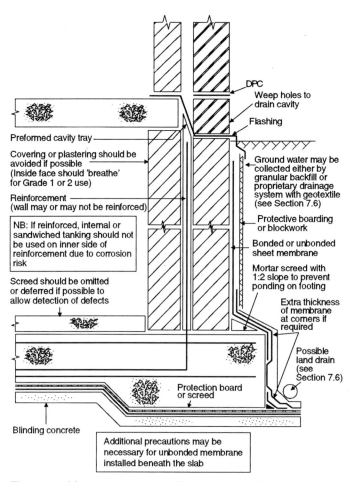

Preformed cavity tray

Covering or plastering should be avoided if possible (Inside face should 'breathe' for Grade 1 or 2 use)

Reinforcement (wall may or may not be reinforced)

NB: If reinforced, internal or sandwiched tanking should not be used on inner side of reinforcement due to corrosion risk

Screed should be omitted or deferred if possible to allow detection of defects

Blinding concrete

DPC

Weep holes to drain cavity

Flashing

Ground water may be collected either by granular backfill or proprietary drainage system with geotextile (see Section 7.6)

Protective boarding or blockwork

Bonded or unbonded sheet membrane

Mortar screed with 1:2 slope to prevent ponding on footing

Extra thickness of membrane at corners if required

Possible land drain (see Section 7.6)

Protection board or screed

Additional precautions may be necessary for unbonded membrane installed beneath the slab

Figure 3.8 Masonry structure with external tanking (Type Ae)

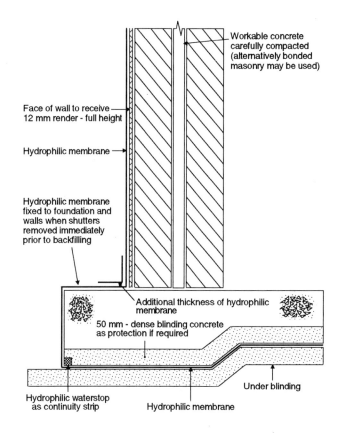

Workable concrete carefully compacted (alternatively bonded masonry may be used)

Face of wall to receive 12 mm render - full height

Hydrophilic membrane

Hydrophilic membrane fixed to foundation and walls when shutters removed immediately prior to backfilling

Additional thickness of hydrophilic membrane

50 mm - dense blinding concrete as protection if required

Under blinding

Hydrophilic waterstop as continuity strip

Hydrophilic membrane

Figure 3.9 Masonry structure with external hydrophilic tanking (Type Ae) (Details similar for other types of structural wall)

Tanking is generally reliable in the medium term (assuming no construction defects), but may be costly to install and requires a skilled contractor. External tanking cannot generally be applied to piled walls or in other situations of restricted access.

3.6.2 Reverse tanking

This is a variation of external tanking where the tanking is applied to a surface prior to construction of the structural elements against it. Figure 3.10 gives an example of the use of reverse tanking where the membrane is applied to the exposed face of sheet piling, or to an existing non-loadbearing external wall, prior to construction of the structural walls against the tanking.

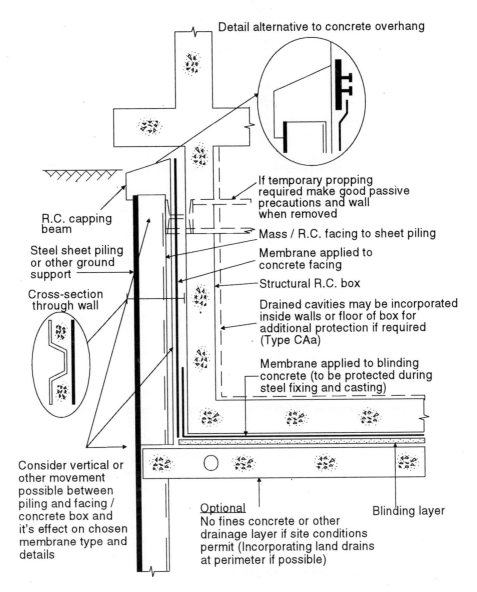

Detail alternative to concrete overhang

If temporary propping required make good passive precautions and wall when removed

Mass / R.C. facing to sheet piling

Membrane applied to concrete facing

Structural R.C. box

Drained cavities may be incorporated inside walls or floor of box for additional protection if required (Type CAa)

Membrane applied to blinding concrete (to be protected during steel fixing and casting)

R.C. capping beam

Steel sheet piling or other ground support

Cross-section through wall

Consider vertical or other movement possible between piling and facing / concrete box and it's effect on chosen membrane type and details

Optional
No fines concrete or other drainage layer if site conditions permit (Incorporating land drains at perimeter if possible)

Blinding layer

Figure 3.10 Example of external tanking applied to inner face of sheet piling (reverse tanking) (Type Ae$_r$)

This method is also commonly used with floor slabs, where an adhesive membrane is applied to the blinding layer and protected by a screed, before the floor slab is cast. The membrane is taken sufficiently far from the edge of the base slab to permit a lap joint to be formed with the wall membrane (see Figure 3.11).

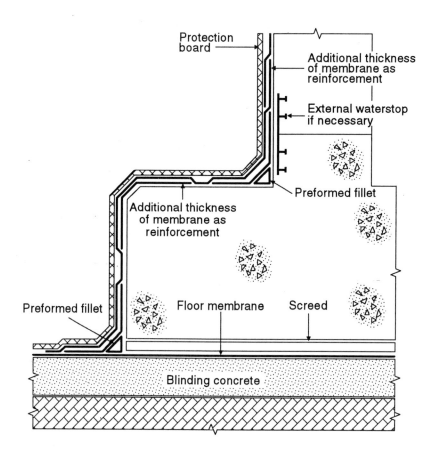

Figure 3.11 Example of jointing between floor and wall; external tanking membranes (Type Ae)

It is important that the effects of any differential movements on the integrity of the waterproofing membrane are considered, particularly at the foot of the wall, as these may be large and continue for some time after the completion of the building.

Reverse tanking would be similar to the use of an unbonded membrane, should a leak occur, in that a potential moisture path exists over the surface of the structure. The risk of damage to the membrane is likely to be greater than for a bonded membrane owing to the greater level of activity adjacent to it while constructing the structural walls and floor. This problem may be avoided by the use of membranes that are initially mechanically fixed, at selvages, to the ground support system, but which bond to concrete poured against them, by means of a specially formulated pressure sensitive adhesive (see also Section 7.3.1.2).

3.6.3   Sandwiched tanking

Figure 3.12 gives an example of this system of protection for a masonry basement.

When sandwiched tanking is used it generally provides a membrane internal to a structural masonry wall and should only be considered when external tanking is impracticable for reasons of construction procedure, access or ground conditions. Whenever sandwiched tanking is installed it should be fully supported by a loading coat of sufficient weight to prevent it from being 'pushed away' from the surface owing to groundwater pressure. A loading coat would probably take the form of a concrete slab on the floor and blockwork for the walls (the cavity between the wall and the membrane being filled with mortar). The loading coat should be constructed as soon as possible after the membrane has been installed.

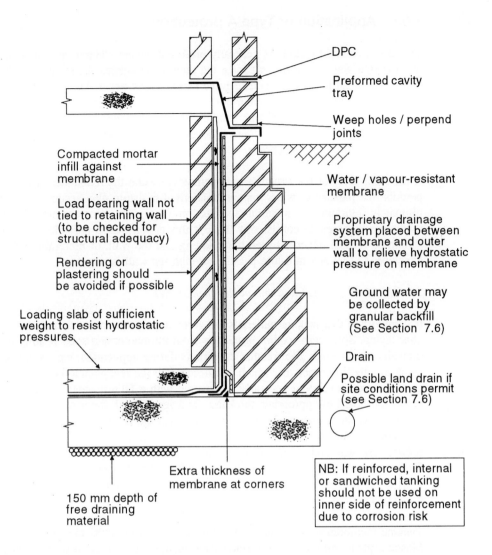

DPC

Preformed cavity tray

Weep holes / perpend joints

Compacted mortar infill against membrane

Load bearing wall not tied to retaining wall (to be checked for structural adequacy)

Rendering or plastering should be avoided if possible

Loading slab of sufficient weight to resist hydrostatic pressures

Water / vapour-resistant membrane

Proprietary drainage system placed between membrane and outer wall to relieve hydrostatic pressure on membrane

Ground water may be collected by granular backfill (See Section 7.6)

Drain

Possible land drain if site conditions permit (see Section 7.6)

Extra thickness of membrane at corners

150 mm depth of free draining material

NB: If reinforced, internal or sandwiched tanking should not be used on inner side of reinforcement due to corrosion risk

Figure 3.12 Masonry structure with sandwiched tanking (Type As)

3.6.4 Internal tanking

An internal tanking membrane is applied to the inside of the structural walls. Consideration must, however, be given to preventing the separation of the membrane from the substrate due to hydrostatic pressure. In the case of applied renders this may be achieved by providing a mechanical anchorage; adhesive sheet membranes may be retained by sandwiching them between the structural wall and a non-structural inner skin.

Where internal walls abut the exterior walls and floor that form the external water-resistant envelope of the basement, the continuity of the membrane must be maintained. This may be achieved by installing the membrane on the outer envelope prior to constructing the inner walls, by incorporating a damp-resistant membrane at the junction, which could be integrated with the tanking membrane when installed, or by continuing the tanking membrane to cover all the faces of the inner walls, where these are small.

3.6.5 Application of Type A protection

The use of external tanking is generally preferred, where site and design conditions permit, so that external water pressure will force the membrane against the structure. Where a permanent hydrostatic head is possible, considerable leakage may occur through defects or if the membrane is punctured. The opportunities to repair external tanking membranes are rare. Where considered necessary the structure should either be designed to resist water penetration (Type B protection), or alternatively to control movement and cracking to a degree that can be reliably accommodated by the membrane.

If the outer layer of the structure is impermeable while the remainder of the wall construction permits free passage of water vapour, condensed moisture may accumulate in the wall, ultimately saturating the material (see Section 3.9.4). This becomes most severe when humidity within the basement is consistently high. If this is considered possible, a ventilated cavity should be formed either between the cladding and the wall, or preferably within the structural envelope, so that any moisture passing through the wall is removed.

3.6.5.1 Sheet (bonded and unbonded) membranes

It is important that tanking materials are given appropriate protection against damage during and after laying. Some also require protection from ultraviolet and solar heating if they are not to be immediately covered. The weather conditions during application, e.g. rain, fog or mist, may result in adhesion problems, which can necessitate the reapplication of primers. The membrane under a base slab should generally be covered with a 50 mm sand/cement screed or non-rotting protection board of appropriate thickness (leakage through the membrane will, however, allow water to use the board as a moisture path beneath the floor slab). On the walls most types of membrane should be covered by protection boards or a blockwork wall leaving a 40 mm gap between the wall and the membrane, which should be filled with mortar as the work proceeds. This may not be the best position for hydrophilic membranes however, as they are intended to react to the presence of water. The membrane manufacturer's recommendations for location and protection should be followed.

Tanking membranes should be made continuous with the DPC to protect the superstructure. Mastic asphalt and bonded preformed sheet membranes adhere to walls, which will theoretically prevent water from spreading in the event of a puncture. Hydrophilic membranes will become bonded after hydration. Bonded membranes are preferred for use under base slabs, not polythene, as they are less susceptible to punctures and will provide more effective lap joints.

All tanking systems require a high quality of care and workmanship during design and construction. The requirements for surface profile and preparation in order to achieve a good bond between the structure and tanking membrane should be considered before final selection of a particular type. The costs and reliability (see Section 3.1.1) of a membrane system should also be considered in conjunction with its application during the construction sequence.

Bonded membranes, where needed, are generally selected for their ease of application and reliability.

3.6.5.2 Hydrophilic membranes

The use of hydrophilic membrane systems (see Section 7.3.1.3(b)) is becoming more common, as they possess many of the advantages of both bonded and unbonded membranes. They are unbonded while being fitted, but subsequently bond to the structure when wetted. They also have self-healing properties, which makes them more tolerant of minor damage during subsequent works. Care must be taken to avoid premature wetting, however, and the basement design should allow for the expansive forces that may be generated during the take-up of water.

In near surface external environments where dehydration and rehydration of the membrane may occur, temporary short-term leakage may result (if other precautions are not included in the environmental control system, e.g. Type B protection), owing to the reduction in water resistance of the membrane while rehydration occurs. The water-resistance properties of the material return on complete rehydration; however, any periods of leakage may not be acceptable for some grades of internal environment.

3.6.5.3 *Cementitious renders*

Multiple-coat cementitious renders can also be used with good effect on residential basements, and other similar applications. The render must be of sufficient thickness to bridge existing cracks or other defects in the substrate. It will not accommodate the movement of 'live' cracks.

3.6.5.4 *Liquid-applied membranes*

Health and safety considerations generally prohibit the use of spray-applied liquid membranes internally.

Internal tanking, with liquid-applied membranes, is not normally considered appropriate for new basements (see Sections 7.3.1.4 and 7.3.2.4).

3.7 TYPE B: STRUCTURALLY INTEGRAL PROTECTION

Type B protection depends on the ability of the structure, by itself, to minimise water penetration. These basements are usually constructed as a reinforced concrete box designed to resist hydrostatic pressure and other loadings. Protection against water penetration relies on the design and construction[3.13] of high-quality concrete, with cracking controlled to prevent the penetration of moisture to an unacceptable degree.

Care should be taken when detailing joints to keep them simple, as details that are difficult to construct are likely to be more prone to leakage and more difficult to rectify. The inclusion of waterstops in construction joints should only be considered where concrete can be effectively compacted around them and their configuration remains unaltered (see Figure 3.13 and Section 7.4). Surface-mounted or hydrophilic waterstops may, for that reason, be preferable to the use of centrally fitted bulb or flat waterstops.

Reinforced concrete designed and constructed to BS8007 or BS8110 can be used in conjunction with Type A or C protection to achieve all grades of internal environment.

3.7.1 Reinforced concrete construction

All grades of basement internal environment can be achieved, at varying cost, utilising any of the three types of passive structure protection (A, B or C) with reinforced concrete (in-situ or piled walls). The merits and disadvantages of each construction type (see Table 3.4) should be evaluated in conjunction with an assessment of the reliability of the system (see Section 3.1.1), particularly the risk of failing to meet the criteria for internal environment for new reinforced concrete, deep or shallow basements, as summarised in Table 3.1.

The degree of water and vapour resistance achievable generally increases with construction costs; however, complete environmental control, by Type B protection alone, cannot be guaranteed in practice for any construction method. Systems with a large number of joint interfaces, e.g. piled walls, are more likely to result in water penetration, but these may be dealt with during construction, or after the addition of a reinforced concrete internal lining wall.

A wide variety of means are available to form basement perimeter walls. These range from temporary support methods, which allow traditional construction techniques to be adopted, to wall types used as either temporary or permanent works.

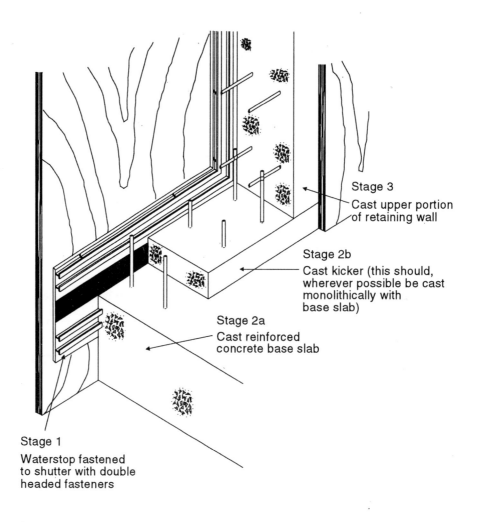

Stage 3
Cast upper portion
of retaining wall

Stage 2b
Cast kicker (this should,
wherever possible be cast
monolithically with
base slab)

Stage 2a
Cast reinforced
concrete base slab

Stage 1
Waterstop fastened
to shutter with double
headed fasteners

Figure 3.13 Typical detail for external waterstop at kicker
of reinforced concrete retaining walls

Methods of basement construction that can be incorporated into the permanent works, using reinforced concrete, are summarised in Table 3.4 and illustrated in Figure 3.14.

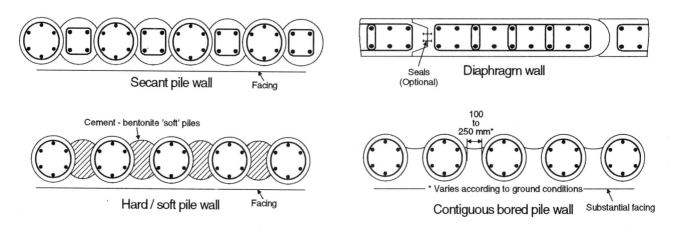

Secant pile wall   Facing

Seals
(Optional)   Diaphragm wall

Cement - bentonite 'soft' piles

Hard / soft pile wall   Facing

100
to
250 mm*

* Varies according to ground conditions

Contiguous bored pile wall   Substantial facing

Figure 3.14 Construction methods for reinforced concrete
basements (excluding monolithic box)

Table 3.4   Considerations for reinforced concrete and structural steel construction methods

Construction type	Construction method	Floors	Walls	Resistance to water or water and vapour penetration	
				Primary precautions	**Secondary precautions**
R.C. box	Open excavation	Monolithic	Integral	Low permeability concrete	External membrane
R.C. box	Temporary steel sheet piling	Monolithic	Integral	Low permeability concrete	Drained protection
Diaphragm walling	Excavate later	Become struts	As cast or faced	Low permeability concrete	Drained protection
Secant piles	Excavate later	Become struts	Facing	Facing	Drained protection
Contiguous piles	Excavate later	Become struts	Substantial facing	Substantial facing	Drained protection
Steel sheet piling	Excavate later	Become struts	Concrete facing	Weld joints	Drained protection

Note: Details of alternative construction methods are given in the Institution of Structural Engineers report on Deep Basements[3.3].

It is important to recognise the difficulties in excluding water from bored pile-walled structures and the high cost penalties involved in attempting to do so. It may be more practical to accept some water penetration, and design for its positive removal (Type C precautions). In using such a system, it is necessary to consider the possible effects of groundwater penetration or of groundwater damming on the surrounding environment and its effect on the hydrology of the surrounding area[3.14].

All single propped bored-pile walls share the same stability requirements; failure modes are illustrated in CIRIA Report 104[3.15], with factors of safety and design criteria being thoroughly discussed for stiff over-consolidated clays (which are equally relevant to other soils).

Guidance on pile type and construction is clearly explained in the CIRIA *Pile Guide* series[3.16]

Example details of the more common forms of reinforced concrete construction are shown in Figures 3.2–3.5 and the combinations of passive precautions associated with integral protection (Type B) are shown in Figure 3.15.

3.7.1.1 Monolithic box

This includes structurally integral reinforced or possibly prestressed concrete floors and walls within open excavation or temporary steel sheet piling or 'soft' contiguous piles. Various temporary works options are available to provide support to the sides of the excavation, enabling conventional construction methods be used to build the permanent structural members.

Temporary works may include:

- open cut
- vertical or trench cut
- sheet piles
- driven steel sections
- permeation grouting
- jet grouting
- soil mixing
- soil nailing.

3.7.1.2 Diaphragm walling

Diaphragm walls are well suited to situations that require large-dimension wall sections, and are more appropriate for permeable soils than other piled wall types.

Care should be taken with detailing the interlocking panels and, attention should be paid to the implications of wall tolerances, particularly horizontally, for the dimensions of the permanent works. The accurate placement of reinforcement cages and 'box-outs' to connect the walls with the floors of the permanent works is also essential.

Where concrete is placed by displacement of bentonite slurry, used to stabilise the excavation, care should be taken to prevent premature withdrawal of tremie tubes as this results in bentonite inclusions in the concrete.

3.7.1.3 Contiguous piled walling

Contiguous piled walling tends to be adopted in clay subsoils, where groundwater flow is limited, as granular materials require deep and expensive temporary casing. Groundwater flow in such clay soils is limited and will not relieve local excess pore pressures. The soil face could theoretically be left exposed but this is seldom undertaken.

Depending on the nature of the soil it may be sufficient to infill the pile cusps with 'no fines' concrete; alternatively a proprietary drainage sheet may be connected to positive drainage at the bottom of the wall, where there is a possibility of water flow and fines being drawn through the wall. It is possible to apply a water-resisting inner skin, but this is seldom economic and often leads to difficult and expensive wall/pile connections.

3.7.1.4 Secant piled walling

Secant walls attempt to replace the need for 'structural' internal walls by intermarrying piles with a good structural bond.

True secant walling (oscillator-formed piles) has been accepted as a reasonable alternative to diaphragm walling in the provision of 'watertight' walling but not, so far, pseudo-secant walls. Typically, cement/bentonite mixes or pfa/cement mixes have been explored for the soft intermediate pile. Insufficient long-term evidence of water exclusion is available to predict design lives, particularly with the use of the more friable bentonite mixes. Attempts to use stronger mixes increase deviation problems with augers, unless the rate of strength development is delayed.

3.7.1.5 Hard/soft piled walling

Hard/soft interlocking piled walls consist of alternate soft 'female piles' formed from combinations of cement, pfa, ggbs, bentonite and other suitable materials and hard 'male piles' of reinforced concrete.

The long-term durability of the wall, particularly where it may be exposed to wetting, drying or freezing cycles, should be checked to determine the need for any permanent lining. This form of retaining wall is generally more suited to basements constructed in granular soils below the water table, where a contiguous bored pile wall may not be appropriate.

3.7.2 Reinforced concrete design

The design of a concrete mix is important, and whether the concrete is site-mixed or ready-mixed it should be produced in accordance with BS5328. To achieve the best result, a compromise must be made between the conflicting requirements of strength, high workability, high aggregate/cement ratio, low water/cement ratio and economy. Where the mix design recommendations in BS8110 and BS8007 differ, preference should be given to the latter, except where aggressive ground conditions are expected.

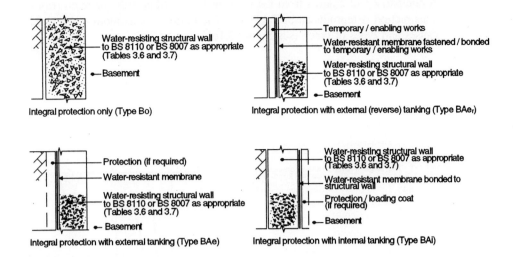

Figure 3.15 Integral protection (Type B)

Experience has shown that crack widths calculated in accordance with the principles adopted by BS8110 may be significantly underestimated (see Section 3.4.2) and structural design to the principles adopted by BS8007 has shown that the factors influencing crack width have a much larger coefficient of variation than the formula for calculating them allows. The principal problems relate to the behaviour of adjacent pours together with 'in-pour' variability of early strength and temperature change. The resulting crack widths can be in the range from zero up to twice the design value. The recommendations for the maximum acceptable leakage rates in BS8007: 1987 : Section 9.2 allow a rate of entry that is barely acceptable even for a Grade 1 basement.

For total crack control it is not sufficient simply to follow the recommendations for reinforcement diameter and spacing in BS8007, as these must be viewed in relation to construction and workmanship factors including:

- overall shape of the structure
- changes in section
- positioning of construction and movement joints
- casting patterns (construction sequence/daywork joints/movement joints)
- restraint from adjacent wall panels, base slab and piles
- control of early thermal and moisture effects by mix design and curing
- out-of-vertical pile problems.

In addition, BS8007 does not cover structures subjected to lateral loads (other than contained liquids), nor the very substantial point loads from columns supporting the superstructure.

From the above it can only be concluded that currently there are no British Standards that cover the particular requirements of concrete basement design and construction. Therefore BS8110 and BS8007 must each be used with caution, with an appreciation of the wider aspects of basement design.

In designing reinforced concrete the following features should be taken into account.

3.7.2.1 Crack widths

For durability reasons (such as limiting reinforcement corrosion) in various environments the maximum crack width occurring at the surface must be controlled.

A comparison of clauses from the relevant British Standards for reinforced concrete basement construction is reproduced in Table 3.5. The limits on maximum crack widths apply to different causes and types of crack (see Figure 3.16).

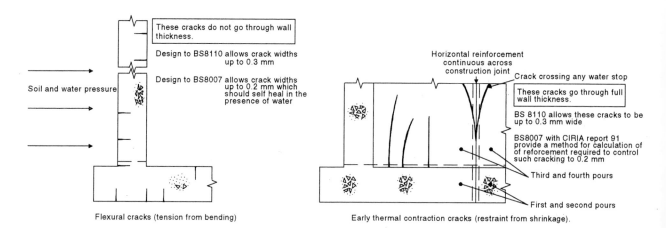

Figure 3.16 Different types of crack in basement construction

Table 3.5   Comparison of British Standard requirements for crack widths in reinforced concrete construction

BS8102: 1990	BS8007: 1987	BS8110: 1985
For Grade 1 basements, design should be to BS8110: Part 2: 1985 with calculated crack widths not exceeding 0.3 mm. For Grades 2, 3 and 4 basements, where reliance is placed upon the structure to prevent the ingress of water, reinforced concrete design and construction should comply with BS8007 and elements should be so proportioned that the concrete strengths and maximum cement contents referred to therein be adhered to.	2.2.3.3 Cracking. For the purpose of defining the serviceability crack width limit state, the maximum design surface crack widths for the exposure conditions defined in **2.7.3** should be taken to be the following. (a) Reinforced concrete. The maximum design surface crack widths for direct tension and flexure or restrained temperature and moisture effects are: (1) severe or very severe exposure: 0.2 mm. (2) critical aesthetic appearance: 0.1 mm. 2.7.3 Exposure and appearance. For the purposes of this code both faces of a liquid-excluding structural member are to be considered as subject to severe exposure as defined in **3.3.4** of BS8110: Part 1: 1985. Surfaces subjected to very severe exposure as defined in **3.3.4** of BS8110: Part 1: 1985 should be designed for a maximum crack width of 0.2 mm (see **2.2.3.3**) and concrete cover and mix complying with the recommendations of BS8110: Part 1: 1985 as well as **2.7.6** and **6.3**.	Part 1, Section 3.3.4 Severe - Concrete surfaces exposed to severe rain, alternate wetting and drying or occasional freezing or severe condensation. Very severe - Concrete surfaces exposed to sea water spray, de-icing salts (directly or indirectly), corrosive fumes or severe freezing conditions whilst wet. Part 2, Section 3.2.4 3.2.4 Excessive cracking. 3.2.4.1 *Appearance*. For members that are visible cracking should be kept within reasonable bounds by attention to detail. As a guide the calculated maximum crack width should not exceed 0.3 mm. 3.2.4.2 *Corrosion*. For members in aggressive environments, the calculated maximum crack widths should not exceed 0.3 mm. 3.2.4.3 *Loss of performance*. Where cracking may impair the performance of the structure, e.g. watertightness, limits other than those given in **3.2.4.1** and **3.2.4.2** may be appropriate.

For Grade 1 basements, BS8102: 1990 states that design should be to BS8110: Part 2: 1985 with calculated crack widths not exceeding 0.3 mm. The requirements for the permanent works of reinforced concrete basement construction to BS8110: Part 2: 1985, Section 3.2.4.3 are vague but do suggest crack width limits lower than 0.3 mm. The 0.1 mm calculated crack width (BS8007: 1987, Section 2.2.3.3 (2) for critical aesthetic appearance) is not likely to be relevant for basements, as it would result in the use of excessive quantities of reinforcement.

There is no guidance in BS8110 for calculating crack widths in relation to minimum quantities of reinforcement, crack spacing, temperature and moisture effects. These criteria are addressed in BS8007: 1987, which gives guidance on the calculation of the frequency and width of cracks.

Table 3.6 sets out the basis for reinforced concrete design and construction for basements, based on the text and Table 3.1 of BS8102: 1990.

Table 3.6   Basis for reinforced concrete design and construction based on BS8102

Internal environment	Minimum design standards		
	Structures requiring protection		Structurally integral protection
	Type A	Type C	Type B[(1)]
Grade 1	BS8110: Part 1	No recommendations given	BS8110: Part 2[(2)]
Grade 2	BS8110: Part 1		BS8007
Grade 3	BS8110: Part 1	BS8110: Part 1	BS8007
Grade 4	BS8110: Part 1	BS8110: Part 1	BS8007

Notes:

1.   Piled walls cannot meet the reinforcement requirements of BS8110 or BS8007 in the horizontal direction and often cannot meet it in the vertical direction

2.   Calculated flexural crack widths not to exceed 0.3 mm; cracking due to thermal and moisture effects not to exceed 0.2 mm as for BS8007.

Table 3.7 sets out an alternative to BS8102 where reinforced concrete is to be used in the presence of hydrostatic pressure and additional reliance placed on the self-healing properties of the structure (autogenous healing) to minimise the ingress of water. This has been adopted in major UK cut-and-cover construction[(3.17)].

The crack width limits set out in Table 3.7 are explained below.

Cracking in concrete will occur in all but the simplest and smallest of structures. In a structure subjected to hydrostatic pressure a crack, of any size, that passes through the section can form a water path, which may result in leakage or wet patches occurring. A compression zone in the section reduces the likelihood of a water path. A waterstop system, if it is intersected by a crack, may provide a conduit for water around the basement and for leakage to occur wherever there is a weakness in the system (see also Sections 3.7.2.5 and 7.4). It is the responsibility of the designer to limit design crack widths to a predetermined size to restrict or prevent water from leaking through the concrete into the basement[(3.3)]. However, this does not preclude the possibility that some cracks will be wider than the calculated characteristic crack width.

Table 3.7   Alternative basis to BS8102 for the design and construction of reinforced concrete basements

Internal environment	Minimum design standards					
	Monolithic box[(1)]			Diaphragm or piled[(2)] walls		
	Type A	Type B	Type C	Type A	Type B	Type C
Grade 1	BS8110	BS8007#	BS8110	Only internal tanking feasible	BS8110	BS8110
Grade 2	BS8007#	BS8007#	BS8110		BS8110	BS8110
Grade 3	BS8007#	BS8007	BS8007#		BS8110	BS8110
Grade 4	BS8007	BS8007	BS8007		BS8110	BS8110

Notes:

1. Calculated maximum design surface crack widths (for the purposes of this table BS8110 refers to BS8110: Part 2: 1985)

    8110   = 0.3 mm flexural, 0.3 mm thermal
    8007#   = 0.3 mm flexural, 0.2 mm thermal
    8007   = 0.2 mm flexural, 0.2 mm thermal

2. Piled walls cannot meet the reinforcement requirements of BS8110 in the horizontal direction and often, cannot meet it in the vertical direction.

The principal causes of cracking are:

1. flexural action, where cracks extend to the neutral axis and are then prevented from growing by a depth of concrete that is in compression, and

2. shrinkage and thermal movement, where cracks tend to be of uniform width through the thickness of the member.

Clearly, the latter type of crack is more likely to allow leakage to occur.

The principal and most effective method to control restrained shrinkage and thermal movement cracking is by the provision of sufficient reinforcement. Additional methods of minimising cracking arising from temperature and moisture changes in concrete structures are outlined in Section 2.6.2.2 of BS8007: 1985. If these are adopted an alternative basis[(3.17)], given in Table 3.7 as BS8007# can be used involving two different calculated surface crack width limits relevant to the different causes of cracking:

1. For cracking due to flexure: 0.3 mm maximum crack width.

2. For cracking due to moisture and/or thermal effects where there may be a loss of performance of the structure due to water leakage: 0.2 mm maximum crack width.

This represents a possible interpretation of Clause 3.2.4.3 of BS8110: Part 2: 1985.

The quantities of reinforcement calculated for flexural design are not additional to those calculated to control thermal cracking. Provided the greatest area of reinforcement is used for either flexure or thermal crack control the design maximum crack widths will be maintained.

For concrete cast in the ground (i.e. piles and diaphragm walls), the early thermal effects are less severe and there is justification for allowing calculated crack widths up to 0.3 mm. However, long-term contraction may be large, which may result in problems with joints and connections with other elements. It is normally acceptable for calculated flexural cracks to be up to 0.3 mm wide[3.18]. In practice both BS8110: Part 2: 1985 and BS8007 should be used in conjunction with CIRIA Report 91[3.13] for calculation of the quantity of reinforcement required to limit thermal and shrinkage cracking.

Design to BS8007 does not guarantee that there will not be any leaking cracks. The implications of reducing the maximum flexural crack width from 0.3 mm to 0.2 mm are a 50% increase in steel reinforcement and a significant increase in cost. Cracks with actual surface crack widths of 0.2 mm, under a hydrostatic pressure of less than 5 m, may heal autogenously so that only damp patches will occur. The reliability of autogenous healing decreases with increasing crack width; hence the contribution of the element to the environmental control system may be lost.

It is important to relate acceptance criteria for concrete basements to water-resistance performance, not to design crack widths. Contingency plans, in the event of cracks leaking, would depend on the internal environment required and the ability of the other elements in the environmental control system adopted to accommodate the moisture ingress. It should be noted that through-cracks where no leakage is currently occurring and for which no remedial actions are proposed (particularly where design has been based on a system of limited environmental control), may not remain dry throughout the life of the structure. Remedial measures that may be considered are outlined in Chapter 5.

3.7.2.2 Internal facings

Facings to piled walls can be directly connected, as in a thin concrete facing, or totally divorced, as in a blockwork cavity skin wall.

3.7.2.3 Changes in section

Changes in section should be avoided if possible as they tend to encourage cracks wider than provided for in calculation.

3.7.2.4 Columns and other point loads

The slab should be sufficiently deep to provide a spread of load to the soil beneath it, without inducing local settlements and the associated distortion. Local thickening of the slab should only be used with caution, as the cost of, and risk of, difficulties created by the change in thickness are likely to cancel any saving attributable to economy of section.

3.7.2.5 Waterstops

If waterstops are to be included (see also Section 7.4), the design of the structure should provide for the continuity of the waterstop system across all joints and particularly junctions between the floor and wall elements (see BS8007: 1987: Figure 5.1 and BS8102: 1990: Figure 20 for typical application details).

External (vertical and horizontal) and hydrophilic waterstops are generally preferred as their design requires no extra precautions in concrete placement. Any pressure against the structure also ensures that external waterstops remain in position after construction.

Internal (vertical and horizontal) waterstops require special attention so as not to dislodge or fold them during placing and compaction of the concrete.

3.7.3   Welded steel sheet piling

Permanent steel sheet piled basements may achieve a Grade 1 (basic utility) and possibly Grade 2 (better utility) internal environment basement under favourable conditions (e.g. low water table controlled by external drainage). The use of steel sheet piling for Grade 3 or 4 internal environments is unlikely to be satisfactory, owing to the difficulties in achieving the high standard of sealing (welding) necessary.

Welded steel sheet piling can be used in most soils, although difficulties in driving may be encountered in dense gravels or stiff clays, or where there are underground obstructions. Where exclusion of groundwater is required, the reliability with which the clutches can be sealed is critical, and is likely to be related to any difficulties with driving. In some locations the level and duration of noise and vibration may influence the selection of this method.

Basement design should consider the total mass of the structure in order to minimise overall settlement as well as risk of flotation. This is particularly important in steel sheet piled basement walls, where the total mass of the basement is much lower and the 'pull-out' resistance of the walls is much less than for concrete piled walls. However, an increase in base slab thickness, to enhance mass, may more than offset the reduction in material mass.

In designing for durability of steel sheet piling it is necessary to consider the following:

3.7.3.1   Corrosion rates of steel

In the absence of concrete protection, the permissible loss in steel thickness, due to corrosion, at the position of maximum stress in the pile should be evaluated in conjunction with predicted rates of corrosion[3.19]. The remaining steel section should enable the basement to achieve the required (60 year minimum) design life.

Under circumstances where corrosion of steel piling is likely to be significant, measures should be taken to increase the life of the structure. These may include:

- the use of additional steel thickness as a 'corrosion allowance'
- the use of high-yield steels at mild steel stress levels, which can enable additional loss in section to be tolerated without loss of load-bearing capacity
- the use of protective coatings, usually paints
- the use of cathodic protection, with or without protective coatings.

3.7.3.2   Sealing/seepage

Sealants must be provided at locks and at the junction between sheet steel piles and the base slab to ensure water resistance. Such sealants must be able to accommodate any movement that will occur during excavation.

A permanent seal on the sheet pile locks would require the provision of a non-structural quick-deposit sealing weld. Its function is to seal the gap between the sheets by forming weld material of the same integrity as the pile in the naturally occurring 'V' formed by the lock. The effective life of a sealing weld will be dependent on the exposure conditions and the weld thickness.

3.7.3.3   Welded steel sheet piling

Grade 1 and 2 basements may be designed using permanent steel sheet piling but are likely to require additional Type C structure protection.

The use of sheet steel piling is unlikely to reliably achieve Grade 3 or 4 internal environments.

3.7.4 Plain concrete and masonry construction

BS8102 states that plain concrete walls should be designed and constructed to comply with the recommendations for mass concrete in Civil Engineering Code of Practice No. 2 (1951). However, the recommendations in BS8110: 1985 for concrete mix design, durability, joints and workmanship should generally be followed.

For new construction, the floor slab should be constructed in concrete and specifically designed to withstand all water pressures that may be imposed on it.

It is not generally considered possible for plain concrete or masonry to provide Type B protection, and for this reason such structures are excluded from the BS8102 Type B structure classification. Plain concrete or masonry construction usually requires Type A and/or Type C protection.

3.7.5 Application of Type B protection

Type B protection alone may achieve Grades 1, 2, and under particular conditions, Grade 3 internal environments. The protection provided to the internal environment is principally influenced by the type of structural materials selected. These can be summarised as follows:

3.7.5.1 Reinforced concrete

Grade 1 or 2 reinforced concrete basements would normally be designed to BS8007: 1987 where they provide integral protection, or with drained protection, or tanking protection added. Reinforced concrete should only be designed to BS8110 where other precautions are to be included in the environmental control system (see Tables 3.1 and 3.6).

Grade 3 or 4 reinforced concrete basements should always be designed to BS8007: 1987, in combination with additional precautions (see Tables 3.1 and 3.6).

3.7.5.2 Welded steel sheet piling

Grade 1 and 2 basements may be designed using permanent steel sheet piling but are likely to require additional Type C structure protection.

The use of sheet steel piling is unlikely to achieve Grade 3 or 4 internal environments reliably.

3.7.5.3 Masonry or plain concrete

Masonry or plain concrete construction, without added structure protection, should generally be restricted to shallow basement construction, without added structure protection, where there is only occasional, or low, hydrostatic pressure.

Grade 1 and 2 internal environments may be achieved using plain concrete or masonry with additional precautions. Where structure protection is required it may be more economical to use reinforced concrete (see Section 3.3).

A Grade 3 environment may be achieved using plain concrete or masonry construction but is likely to require a vapour-resistant barrier as well as drained protection.

A Grade 4 basement should only be constructed using reinforced concrete with some additional structure protection (see Section 3.3).

3.8   TYPE C: DRAINED CAVITY PROTECTION

For successful application of Type C protection, the structural walls must minimise water
penetration. The cavity should not be used to conceal large leaks. Structural walls may be in
plain or reinforced concrete, masonry or steel sheet piling. Any moisture that does penetrate the
structural wall is collected within the cavity created by the addition of an inner skin to the walls
and/or the floor and is discharged to a sump.

A drained cavity system may be used in conjunction with:

- plain concrete or masonry construction
- reinforced concrete (in-situ or piled) construction
- steel sheet piling.

Type C may also be used in conjunction with Type A or B protection (see Figure 3.17).

3.8.1   Drained cavity walls

The inner wall in drained cavities is generally non-load bearing and may need to be designed to
be free-standing to prevent moisture paths occurring across ties. Vapour transmission through
the fabric of the inner wall may be reduced by providing a vapour-resistant membrane, adequate
ventilation of the cavity (mechanically assisted where necessary) or by using a profiled cavity
drainage former, which provides an integral vapour barrier (see Figures 3.2, 3.3, 3.5 and 3.18
(detail A)). The latter method cannot be used with wall ties.

Adequate ventilation of the cavity may require a low level vent. Such ventilation of the cavity
may increase the quantity of water vapour entering the basement (see Figures 3.18 and 3.19).
Where inadequate ventilation of the cavity occurs, owing to the absence of a low level vent, or
for other reasons, a vapour barrier may be necessary as a part of the inner wall construction. In
such cases, any cover to an opening provided for maintaining the channel, should be sealed.

Profiled cavity drainage systems may be used to form cavities within walls and when used, will
reduce the width of the cavity and if the joints are fully sealed will also prevent moisture
bridging across the wall cavity. However, it is necessary that the cavity width is uniform to
contain the system and should not be considered where a non-vertical external wall is a
possibility.

Drained cavities are usually necessary for Grade 3 or 4 internal environments (Table 3.1). The
basement cavity ventilation of larger buildings must also be designed with fire compartments
where these are required by the fire regulations.

3.8.2   Drained cavity floors

Cavities under floors may be formed from no-fines concrete (where seepage is comparatively
slight) or proprietary systems such as profiled drainage sheets or purpose-made tiles (see Figure
3.18 (detail B). An advantage of cavity drainage formers is that they are shallower than
conventional methods, requiring less excavation, and are quicker to install. If the joints are
sealed they may also form a vapour barrier.

Wider cavities may be formed using precast concrete planks to give a raised floor, which may
be useful where access is required e.g for maintenance of drainage channels or for servicing
pumps.

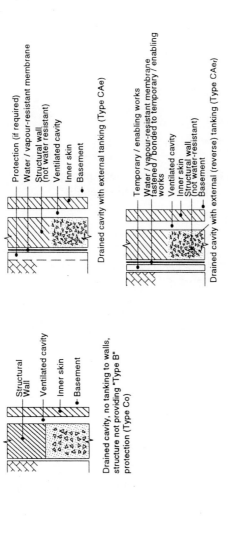

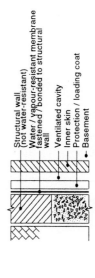

Water-resisting structural wall
to BS 8110 or as appropriate
(Tables 3.6 and 3.7)
Ventilated cavity
Inner skin
Basement

Drained cavity with integral protection only (Type CBo)

Protection (if required)
Ventilated cavity
Water / vapour-resistant membrane
Inner skin
Water-resisting structural wall
to BS 8007 or as appropriate
(Tables 3.6 and 3.7)
Basement

Drained cavity with integral protection and external tanking (Type CBAe)

Temporary / enabling works
Ventilated cavity
Water / vapour resistant membrane
fastened / bonded to temporary / enabling
works
Inner skin
Basement

Drained cavity with integral protection and
external (reverse) tanking (Type CBAer)

Water-resisting structural wall
to BS 8110 or BS 8007 as appropriate
(Tables 3.6 and 3.7)
Ventilated cavity
Water / vapour-resistant membrane
fastened / bonded to structural wall
Inner skin
Protection / loading coat
Basement

Drained cavity with integral protection and internal tanking (Type CBAi)

Structural
Wall
Ventilated cavity
Inner skin
Basement

Drained cavity, no tanking to walls,
structure not providing "Type B"
protection (Type Co)

Protection (if required)
Water / vapour-resistant membrane
Structural wall
(not water resistant)
Ventilated cavity
Inner skin
Basement

Drained cavity with external tanking (Type CAe)

Temporary / enabling works
Water / vapour-resistant membrane
fastened / bonded to temporary / enabling
works
Ventilated cavity
Inner skin
Structural wall
(not water-resistant)
Basement

Drained cavity with external (reverse) tanking (Type CAer)

Two leaves of structural
wall (not tied)
Water / vapour-resistant membrane
Ventilated cavity
Inner skin
Basement

Drained cavity with sandwiched tanking (Type CAs)

Structural wall
(not water-resistant)
Water / vapour-resistant membrane
fastened / bonded to structural
wall
Ventilated cavity
Inner skin
Protection / loading coat
Basement

Drained cavity with internal tanking (Type CAi)

Figure 3.17 Drained cavity protection (Type C)

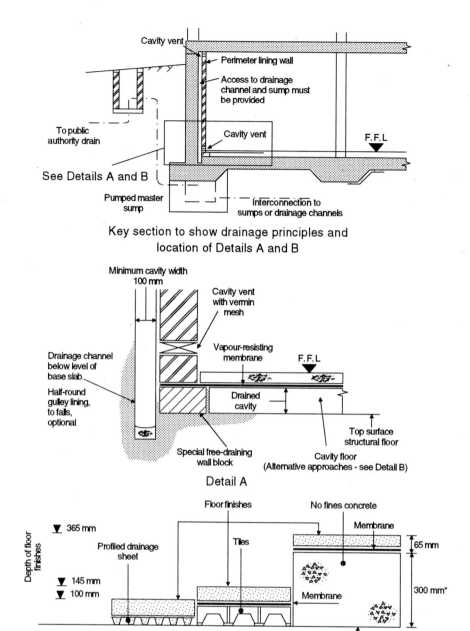

Key section to show drainage principles and location of Details A and B

Detail A

Detail B

Figure 3.18 Cavity drainage details

3.8.3 Advantages of Type C protection

The principal advantages of drained protection are:

- It is less dependent on primary construction processes, which are more difficult to control, and hence is likely to be more reliable in achieving the required environment.
- Installation of the drainage layer can be undertaken in favourable conditions and outside the construction programme critical path.
- Uncertain labour elements are removed.
- Water ingress through the primary structure may be checked and remedied before final installation of the inner wall.

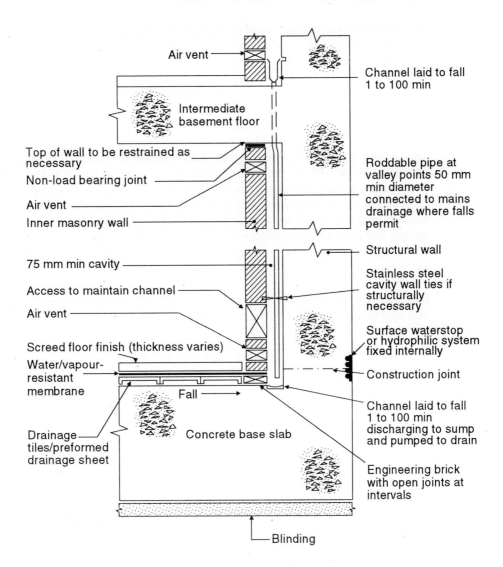

Figure 3.19 Concrete structure with drained wall and floor cavity (Type CBo)

Labels in figure:

Air vent

Intermediate basement floor

Top of wall to be restrained as necessary

Non-load bearing joint

Air vent

Inner masonry wall

75 mm min cavity

Access to maintain channel

Air vent

Screed floor finish (thickness varies)

Water/vapour-resistant membrane

Fall

Drainage tiles/preformed drainage sheet

Concrete base slab

Blinding

Channel laid to fall 1 to 100 min

Roddable pipe at valley points 50 mm min diameter connected to mains drainage where falls permit

Structural wall

Stainless steel cavity wall ties if structurally necessary

Surface waterstop or hydrophilic system fixed internally

Construction joint

Channel laid to fall 1 to 100 min discharging to sump and pumped to drain

Engineering brick with open joints at intervals

3.8.4 Disadvantages of Type C protection

The principal disadvantages of drained protection are:

- There is a reduction of usable floor area, though this can be minimised by the use of profiled drainage formers.
- Pumps will need to be installed to remove accumulated water.
- If the outer skin is of masonry or plain concrete, under a high hydrostatic pressure, water may penetrate the cavity in excessive quantities, which may not be efficiently drained.
- Access to the external wall for repair will be prevented, after the inner wall has been built.
- Costs of pumping, maintenance of pumps, inspection and cleaning of cavities must be accepted.

3.8.5 Application of Type C protection

In conjunction with masonry or plain concrete, in drained site conditions, drained cavity construction alone without a membrane may achieve the requirements of Grades 1 and 2 environments. In conjunction with either Type A or B protection, drained cavity construction may achieve Grade 3 or 4 internal environments. Further details of proprietary internal drainage systems are given in Section 7.7.

3.8.5.1 Reinforced (in-situ or piled) concrete construction

The addition of a drained cavity to reinforced concrete construction for deep or shallow basements can provide the additional protection necessary to satisfy higher grades of internal environment. Drained protection can also be of benefit when used in conjunction with construction that may not fully comply with all the BS8110 or BS8007 requirements. For example, diaphragm walling, contiguous or secant piled walls may not comply in respect of spacing and percentage of reinforcement for crack control. Figure 3.19 gives an example of drained protection for a concrete basement and Figure 3.20 gives an example for a masonry basement.

Drained cavity protection used in conjunction with either Type A and/or B passive protection may also be used to achieve Grades 3 or 4 internal environments.

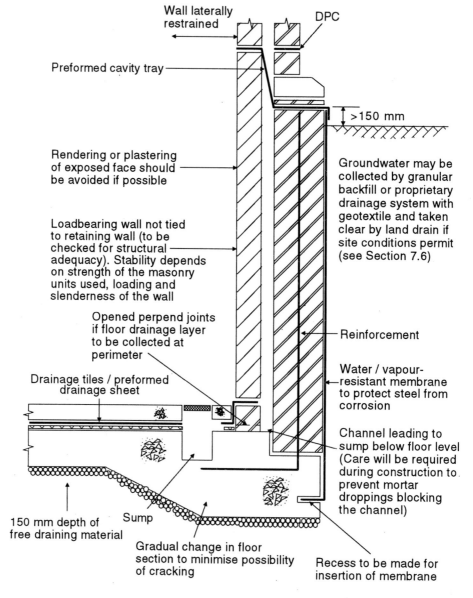

Figure 3.20 Masonry structure with drained cavity (Type CAe)

3.8.5.2 Welded steel sheet piling

Drained protection may be used in conjunction with sheet steel piled primary walls to achieve Grade 1 or 2 internal environments.

3.8.5.3 Masonry or plain concrete

Masonry or plain concrete construction should be restricted to shallow basements for Grade 1 or 2 internal environments in less onerous ground conditions.

Drained cavity protection used in conjunction with Type A protection may be used to achieve a Grade 3 internal environment.

3.9 ACTIVE PRECAUTIONS (HEATING AND VENTILATION)

Selection of the most appropriate form of passive water and vapour protection (Type A, B or C), as outlined in Sections 3.2 to 3.8, is the preliminary step to considering the active precautions required to achieve the desired category of internal environment. The wide variety of possible uses within each grade necessitates that the heating and ventilation system be designed to suit the expected requirements of the particular basement, rather than its nominal grade.

After agreeing the required internal environment (Grade 1-4; see Section 3.1) and establishing the likely groundwater conditions (see Sections 2.2 and 2.3) and the passive protection types thought to be most suitable (see Sections 3.2 to 3.8), it is then necessary to assess whether the basement would comply with ventilation, thermal transmission and resistance to moisture penetration requirements. The minimum performance requirements of the Building Regulations and guidance on the quantification of the functional environmental requirements for different levels of usage (Table 2.2) should be considered.

Evaluation of heating and ventilation requirements should take account of the effectiveness of the passive precautions, the size of the basement (including individual rooms) and the emissions (gaseous and liquid) from machinery and/or human activity. Selected illustrations of the diversity of requirements that can arise within each grade are given in Table 3.8.

This section and its appendices provide only an introduction to heating and ventilation design and deal only with the case of a homogeneous slab. They do not cover the design of joint details, general detailing or workmanship.

Once a decision has been made as to the usage of the basement, basement dimensions and the general form of construction, building services engineers in conjunction with the structural design team should design the heating and ventilation system.

3.9.1 Ventilation

The ventilation requirement is defined as the amount of outdoor air (fresh air) needed to meet the design criteria associated with the building use, and should not be confused with the air circulation rate. The air circulation rate is the total quantity of air supplied to a space. In many systems the room air supply is a mixture of outdoor and recirculated air. Natural ventilation alone is usually insufficient within a basement, as it is dependent on the effects of wind and the difference in air temperature between the inside and outside of a building.

The requirements of the Building Regulations must be taken into consideration for residential basements. Guidance is given in Approved Documents C and F, where clause F1 states:

'There shall be adequate means of ventilation provided for people in the building.'

Table 3.8   Heating and ventilation considerations for selected basement use

Grade of basement	Design for:	
	Ventilation purpose	**Thermal transmittance**
Grade 1 (basic utility) Car parking	Vehicle emissions, oil and gasoline fumes	Heating and insulation generally not required
Plant-rooms (equipment not sensitive to moisture).	Equipment emissions	Heating and insulation may be necessary
Grade 2 (better utility). Plant-rooms (equipment sensitive to moisture)	Equipment emissions	Heating and insulation may be required to limit condensation
Retail storage	Little or no ventilation necessary	Heating necessary, insulation may be required
Grade 3 (habitable) Offices	Human activity (smoking, respiration, etc.)	Heating necessary, insulation may be required
Residential, restaurants	Human activity (as above) and from bathrooms, kitchens, etc.	Heating and insulation essential
Leisure centres	Similar to residential and offices	Heating usually required, insulation may be required
Grade 4 (special) Archive rooms	Ventilation may be required	Heating and insulation essential (strictly controlled internal environment)
Underground bunkers	See Grade 3 requirements	Heating and insulation essential

This is further supplemented by basic performance objectives in Approved Document F, which states:

'In the Secretary of State's view the requirement of F1 will be met if ventilation is provided which under normal conditions is capable, if used, of restricting the accumulation of such moisture (which could lead to mould growth) and pollutants (originating within a building) as would otherwise become a hazard to the health of people in the building.

In order to encourage its use the ventilation should not affect necessary security or comfort to a significant extent.'

Approved Document F also recommends provisions for the extraction of moisture and the size of openings for natural or mechanical ventilation. Further guidance on targets for internal environments is given in Section 2.2, Table 2.2.

The ventilation requirements for each of the internal environment Grades 1 to 4 are described in detail in Appendix C.

3.9.2 Thermal transmittance

The construction of all wall/floor slabs needs to conform to the Building Regulations (Approved Document L), which require a thermal transmittance (U) value of not greater than 0.45 W/m^{2}K. The floor slabs will be constructed of either concrete or masonry, will be bedded on a blinding layer of sand or lean-mix concrete, and may be overlaid with a sand/cement or polymer screed. Floor and wall construction often includes insulation and a vapour barrier.

Insulation is essential and floor insulation must be load-bearing. A 50 mm thickness of insulating material is usually satisfactory. The position of the insulating layer may be arranged to maximise the depth of the structure available for heat storage as in Figure 3.21 or to limit the structure heat storage capacity as in Figure 3.22.

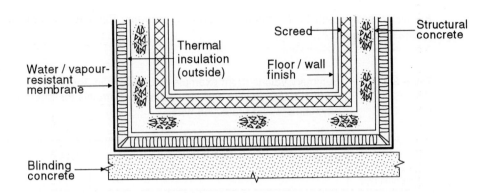

Figure 3.21 Insulating layer positioned to maximise the depth of structure available for heat storage

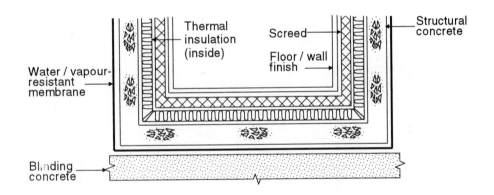

Figure 3.22 Insulating layer positioned to minimise the depth of structure available for heat storage

When properly applied thermal insulation will retard the flow of heat by conduction and will thus serve one or more of the following functions:

- conserving energy by reducing heat loss or gains
- controlling surface temperatures of the structure
- preventing vapour condensation on surfaces by raising the temperature to above the dew-point of the surrounding atmosphere
- reducing temperature fluctuations by virtue of the thermal mass of the fabric within an insulated enclosure when heating or cooling is either not needed or not available
- impeding water vapour transmission.

Example calculations for thermal transmittance and insulation required for a basement are given in Appendix C and summarised in Table 3.9 for the following structures:

- Type A protection in concrete; Grade 1 use (car park)
- Type A protection in concrete; Grade 3 use (residential)
- Type A protection in masonry; Grade 1 use (car park)
- Type B protection in concrete; Grade 1 use (car park)
- Type C protection in concrete; Grade 3 use (residential/office).

Advice on how to satisfy the requirements of the Building Regulations is given in a BRE information paper[3.20].

Table 3.9 Summary values (from example calculations in Appendix C) for moisture loss, thermal transmittance and insulation requirements for different grades of internal environment and protection type

Basement passive protection type	Type A			Type B	Type C
Structure description	Concrete + membrane		Masonry + membrane	Reinforced concrete box	Concrete + cavity wall
Environment and usage	Grade 1 car park	Grade 3 residential	Grade 1 car park	Grade 1 car park	Grade 3 residential
Moisture loss (kg/m^2) (1)					
Summer	0.1	0.1	0.19	0.17	0.165
Winter	-0.03			-0.06	
Thermal transmittance (W/m^{2}K)					
Wall	0.983	0.983	1.05	1.24	0.66
Floor	0.843	0.993		0.853	0.59
Insulation (mm) (2)					
Wall	48	48	47	56	28
Floor	42	46	-	42	21

(1) The moisture loss is the average of all the values calculated for the wall and floors taken over a 60-day period

(2) Insulation requirement is based on phenolic foam, and the tabulated figure is the required thickness of foam to bring the thermal transmittance (U value) up to the Building Regulations value of not greater than 0.45 W/m^{2}K.

3.9.3 Vapour barrier

Most solid materials permit the diffusion of water vapour to some extent, and whenever there is a difference in the vapour pressure across the material, a movement of water vapour takes place. The principal source of water vapour in a basement will be via evaporation of ground moisture from walls and floor surfaces. The use of a vapour barrier may be a more cost-effective and practical method of controlling moisture than by active mechanical ventilation.

3.9.4 Moisture transfer and condensation

Typical moisture losses are illustrated by the example calculations in Appendix C and described above. In Table 3.9, the approximate 60 day losses are given on the basis that there are approximately equal floor and wall areas.

Moisture transfer is dependent upon gains from:

- latent load from occupants
- process load from any products that give up moisture
- exposed water surfaces
- open gas flames
- water vapour migration through gaps around doors
- moisture transmitted from wall and floor surfaces.

Condensation is the change from gas to liquid, and may cause moisture problems. Water vapour condenses when the temperature of the air/vapour mixture falls below the dew-point, a consequence of either:

- vapour flow to a region of lower temperature, or
- a reduction in surface temperature.

Design for heating and ventilation should ensure that there is no internal and/or interstitial condensation, as shown in Figure 3.23. Interstitial condensation can be avoided if ventilation is provided internally to vapour permeable walls or floors (Types B or C protection).

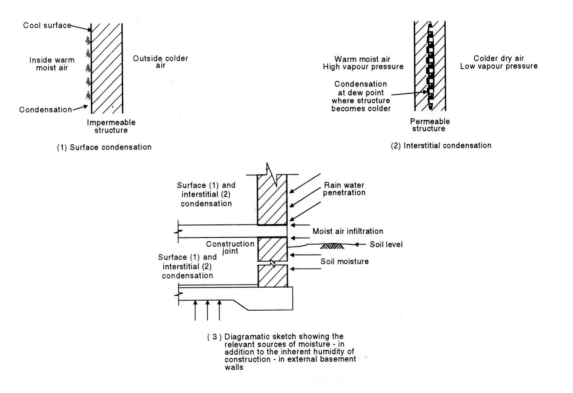

Figure 3.23 Surface and interstitial condensation and moisture sources in external walls

If the outer surface is impermeable (Type A protection) and the basement is not heated or ventilated, condensed moisture may accumulate in the wall and ultimately saturate the material. The situation is most severe where high internal relative humidity occurs.

A vapour-resistant membrane (Type A protection) on the inner face of the basement walls (the potentially warmer side) is relied upon to prevent moisture penetration into the basement from the ground through the walls and floor. The structural materials must not deteriorate by being saturated and should be adequate to resist the forces induced by temperature gradients through them.

Condensation will only occur where the permeability of the walls or floor allows sufficiently moist air to penetrate to a position sufficiently cold to produce dew-point conditions. Calculation methods exist for determining this[3.21-27] but three guiding principles can be stated as follows:

1.   The design of the active precautions should ensure that the provision of a vapour barrier does not cause internal and/or interstitial condensation. Prevention of water or vapour penetration by an internal vapour-resistant membrane (Type A) or internal drained cavity (Type C) may not require precautions against condensation.

2.   Although completely impermeable vapour barriers at the inside surface are difficult to achieve, a partial vapour penetration calculation is still useful.

3.   Where a number of different layers make up a construction, as much of the structure as possible should be kept warm. Where it is not easy to apply barrier treatments, insulation materials are better placed towards the outer face, but they must be protected from groundwater. If the bulk of insulation is to be positioned at the inner face, it may be necessary to protect the warm side by a vapour barrier, or carry out a vapour penetration calculation.

3.10   DESIGN APPROVAL

Agreement with the client on the design objectives for the basement (Section 3.1) should establish:

- the requirements for the internal environment (including quantified limits on leakage where appropriate)
- the budgetary controls and constraints on the work
- whether a system of limited or complete protection is to be employed to achieve the aims of the above.

Throughout the design phase the client should be informed of any significant factors likely to affect the protection system and, on completion of the design, the designer should obtain the approval of the client, for the system proposed. A formal agreement should describe:

- what the system, realistically, can be expected to achieve and the costs likely to be associated with it
- capital, maintenance and operating costs for complete protection
- contingency plans for repair or upgrading (see Chapter 5) of a system of limited protection should it be chosen and become inadequate at some future time.

The designer should assess the likely worst instances of failure of the system that will need to be allowed for and inform the client.

Formal design approval should therefore establish:

- how a target internal environment, with moisture ingress not exceeding defined limits (including contingency plans for leakage in a system of limited protection, see Section 3.1), will be achieved, and that

- the client will arrange to fund the future operating costs (heating, ventilation and maintenance, etc.) for a system of complete protection or the direct and indirect costs of possible future repairs to a system of limited protection.

REFERENCES

3.1   BUILDING RESEARCH ESTABLISHMENT
       Construction of new buildings on gas-contaminated land
       BRE Report 212, 1991

3.2   BUILDING RESEARCH ESTABLISHMENT
       Radon: guidance on protective measures for new dwellings
       BRE Report 211, 1991

3.3   THE INSTITUTION OF STRUCTURAL ENGINEERS
       Design and construction of deep basements
       The Institution of Structural Engineers, in preparation

3.4   HMSO
       The Building Regulations 1991 (SI 1991 No. 2765) effective from 1 June 1992
       replacing The Building Regulations 1985 (SI 1985 No. 1065)

       The Building Regulations 1991, Approved Documents:

B2/3/4	Fire spread	1992 Edition
C1/2/3/4	Site preparation and contaminants	1992 Edition
C4	Resistance to weather and ground moisture	1992 Edition
D1	Cavity insulation	1985 Edition
F1	Means of ventilation	1995 Edition
F2	Condensation	1995 Edition
H1	Sanitary pipework and drainage	1990 Edition
H3	Rainwater drainage	1990 Edition
L1	Conservation of fuel and power	1995 Edition
M	Access for the disabled	1992 Edition
Amendments		1992

3.5   BRITISH STANDARDS INSTITUTION
       Code of practice for protection of buildings against water from the ground [except for those sections superseded by BS8102: 1990]
       CP102: 1973

3.6   BRITISH STANDARDS INSTITUTION
       Code of practice for protection of structures against water from the ground
       BS8102: 1990

3.7   HMSO
       Determination C4, Whether the walls and floor would adequately resist the passage of water vapour
       Department of the Environment, Appeals and Determinations, June 1991

3.8   BRITISH STANDARDS INSTITUTION
       Code of practice for structural use of concrete
       BS8110: 1985

3.9   BRITISH STANDARDS INSTITUTION
        Code of practice for design of concrete structures for retaining aqueous liquids
        BS8007: 1987

3.10   BRITISH STANDARDS INSTITUTION
        Code of practice for use of masonry: Part 3, Materials and components, design and workmanship
        BS5628: 1985

3.11   JOHNSON, R.A., LEEK, D.S. and KING, E.S.
        Waterproofing and repairing underground reservoir roofs
        CIRIA Technical Note 145, 1991

3.12   MASTIC ASPHALT COUNCIL & EMPLOYERS FEDERATION
        Tanking handbook
        MACEF, 1990

3.13   HARRISON, T.A.
        Early-age thermal crack control in concrete
        CIRIA Report 91, 1993

3.14   EDWARDS, J.T. (Ed.)
        Civil engineering for underground rail transport
        Butterworth & Co (Publishers) Ltd, 1990

3.15   PADFIELD, C.J. and MAIR R.J.
        Design of retaining walls embedded in stiff clays
        CIRIA, Report 104 (1984)

3.16   CONSTRUCTION INDUSTRY RESEARCH AND INFORMATION ASSOCIATION
        Piling Group, Pile Guides 1 to 9
        CIRIA, PSA, DoE, PG1 to PG9, 1977/1988

3.17   POWDERHAM, A.J.
        Cut and cover design and construction in reinforced concrete
        Civil Engineering for Underground Rail Transportation, Chapter 6, p 142, Butterworth Ltd., 1990

3.18   DUGGLEBY, J.C., AVGHERINOS, P.J. and POWDERHAM, A.J.
        Channel Tunnel: Foundation engineering at the UK portal
        Proceedings of the 4th International Conference on Piling and Deep Foundations, Stresa, Italy, April 1991, Volume 1.

3.19   MORLEY, J.
        A review of the underground corrosion of steel piling
        British Steel Corporation, Teeside Laboratories, BSC Report T/CS/1114/1/1/78/C

3.20   BUILDING RESEARCH ESTABLISHMENT
        U values for basements
        BRE, Information Paper 14/94, 1994

3.21   CHARTERED INSTITUTION OF BUILDING SERVICES ENGINEERS
        Guides: Volumes A, B and C
        CIBSE, London, 1987

3.22   AMERICAN SOCIETY OF HEATING REFRIGERATION & AIR CONDITIONING ENGINEERS INC.
        ASHRAE Handbook: Fundamentals, SI Edition
        ASHRAE, Atlanta, 1989

3.23   AMERICAN SOCIETY OF HEATING REFRIGERATION & AIR CONDITIONING
        ENGINEERS INC.
        ASHRAE Handbook Applications
        ASHRAE, Atlanta, 1978

3.24   AMERICAN SOCIETY OF HEATING REFRIGERATION & AIR CONDITIONING
        ENGINEERS INC.
        ASHRAE Handbook Systems
        ASHRAE, Atlanta, 1978

3.25   MINISTRY OF PUBLIC BUILDING AND WORKS
        Condensation in dwellings. Part 1: A design guide
        HMSO

3.26   BUILDING RESEARCH ESTABLISHMENT
        Condensation
        BRE, Digest 110, 1972

3.27   BUILDING RESEARCH ESTABLISHMENT
        Ventilation of internal bathrooms and WCs in dwellings
        BRE, Digest 170, 1984

4   External drainage provisions

Where access to the ground outside the basement is possible, and means of discharge are available, drainage to control the external groundwater level may be provided.

When the groundwater flow is expected to be away from the basement, it is beneficial to lower the water table in the vicinity of the structure, as this greatly reduces the hydrostatic head and consequently the risk of water entering through defects. However, the effects on adjacent properties of lowering the water table should also be considered as (particularly in silt and clay soils) substantial changes in bearing capacity and settlements may be induced. Significant ground movements in the ground adjacent to excavations can be expected to extend, laterally, to more than three times the depth of the excavation[4.1].

The use of granular backfill, or a profiled plastic drainage sheet around the exterior of the structure will reduce the hydrostatic head *only* if provision is made to drain water *from* the fill.

One possible disadvantage of providing an inadequately drained permeable layer (or sheet) is that it will provide a continuous supply of water *to* any defective areas of the protection system, exacerbating leaks. This can also occur when the granular backfill (in excavations around basements) is more permeable than the surrounding undisturbed soil and acts as a reservoir for water surrounding the structure.

Even where it is not practicable to install external wall drainage, as for example when diaphragm walling or piling is used, it is still worthwhile considering the construction of a drainage layer beneath the floor slab, where the ground is of low permeability, as this may reduce the water pressure on the wall/floor joint. For larger basements, open-jointed pipes or fin drains can be incorporated within the drainage layer to collect and conduct water between piles. This permits a reduction in the thickness of the drainage layer while still providing the same hydraulic gradient.

Geotextile filters may be used in silty soils to slow, or prevent blockage of drains. Profiled 'dimpled' plastic sheet systems are also available with a geotextile filter bonded to them. For further details of materials see Section 7.6. It is important to consider the long-term efficacy of any drainage system provided.

Drainage can reduce the uplift and lateral loads that may be imposed on the structure, but it is unwise to assume that the drains will operate efficiently indefinitely. Guidance on the minimum water level to be considered for structural design are given in Section 3.4 of BS8102: 1990:

'(a) Monolithic structures are to be preferred in that they are better able to resist the varying conditions imposed by the relatively indeterminate nature of subsoil earth and water pressures.
(b) For basements not exceeding 4 m deep a design head of groundwater, three-quarters the full depth below ground (subject to a minimum of 1 m), is usually adequate.
(c) For deeper basements the water table should be taken as being 1 m below ground level.
(d) In addition to simple water pressure, allowance should be made for the additional pressure of the submerged earth, the loading effects of adjoining buildings or any heavy ground surface loading against the boundary of the building.
(e) The structure should be checked for flotation at various stages of construction and temporary arrangements to balance water pressures may have to be considered.
(f) Any improvements to the waterproofing of an existing structure may increase the water pressure upon it and this should be checked.'

This advice is intended to ensure structural adequacy. If water cannot stand at the depth stated or if even higher water levels are possible, then the hydrostatic head to be used in the design should be assessed for the particular circumstances.

REFERENCES

4.1   BURLAND, J.B. and HANCOCK, R.J.R.
Underground car park at the House of Commons, London: geotechnical aspects
BRE, CP 13/77, March 1977

5 Improving the water-resistance of existing basements

Improvements may be carried out to either:

1.   achieve the required internal environment reliably, or

2.   improve the existing grade of internal environment.

The current condition of the structure will need to be established in each case to determine the requirements for the repairs or upgrading. The procedures that may be employed and data required from the investigation are described in Section 5.1.

Maintenance of the present grade of internal environment by the repair of defects due to deterioration of the existing waterproofing is considered below.

The remedial treatment of defects in new works is also considered where the required grade can be achieved by localised, relatively minor, repair work. Where (in new construction) the achieved environment (grade) is significantly below that required, work should be more properly regarded as an improvement in grade.

Many existing basements in poor condition (often constructed from masonry with no water or vapour protection) have been taken out of use and backfilled. This is a waste of resources when techniques exist for internal treatment (e.g. water-resistant renders) that can return them to use, at least for non-sensitive storage (Grade 1). If reduced space is acceptable, then the addition of drained cavities to walls and floors, together with the provision of adequate insulation, heating and ventilation can upgrade basements to residential standards (Grade 3). It is possible to achieve special (Grade 4) environments with existing techniques, but the cost may be prohibitive.

The methods and materials available to improve the internal environment are described in Section 5.3. This section would also be applicable where an existing basement has no effective waterproofing and is to be upgraded, or where the internal environment achieved in new construction falls far short of that required, and large-scale remedial works are necessary to correct the deficiency.

The logic path showing the stages required in the maintenance/upgrading of the internal environment of the basement is illustrated in Figure 3.1, and examples of the additional passive precautions available to improve or upgrade the control of the internal environment are given in Table 5.1.

5.1   INVESTIGATION OF THE CURRENT CONDITION

Defective basement 'waterproofing' may become apparent during the later stages of the building works or the initial period of occupation (as external water levels rise due to permeation and pressures equilibrate) or later, during occupancy, by the evidence of gradual deterioration of the applied finishes on the walls and floor, or an increase in the quantity of water being collected by cavity and other internal drainage.

In order to assess the requirements for remedial works to the basement it is necessary to confirm the intended internal environment (see Sections 2.2 and 3.1), the method of construction (see Section 3.3), and the passive protection system adopted (see Sections 3.6 to 3.8), and to determine the location, nature and extent of the defects in the structure[5.1]. The extent of heating and ventilation should also be considered (see Section 3.9) and any necessary calculations undertaken or checked. This may be relatively easy for recent works where contract drawings and documentation are still available, but in older structures this may require substantial investigation.

The environmental control system of an existing basement may not be able to cope with a rise in groundwater level.

In many cases (particularly defective structures with Type B protection) the water entry points will be readily visible on the surface of the walls and/or floor where leakage is occurring at macrodefects (e.g. cracks in concrete), or breakdown of mortar joints, etc. The investigation should determine whether water is penetrating the basement walls and/or floor and the precise source of the leak. This is important as the decision regarding the selection of remedial methods may be strongly influenced by whether there is ingress through the floor. Particular attention should be paid to the possibility of transmission through defective pipe services, along service ducts or through the floor slab at column or pile positions and particularly at doorways and loading bays.

In other instances, where the failure to achieve the required grade of internal environment can only be detected as excessive RH levels, the locations of moisture (vapour) ingress may be more difficult to detect. Care will need to be taken to distinguish between moisture that penetrates through the structure of the basement, moisture that originates from the construction materials in the early life of the basement (particularly the drying out of concrete, mortar or porous bricks which may have been saturated prior to construction), and condensation due to inadequate ventilation (see Section 3.9). This may require long-term monitoring of the vapour levels within the structure and construction materials to quantify the internal environment (see Section 2.2).

The external environment will also need to be classified and quantified in accordance with Table 2.3, particularly for older structures, which may be affected by rising groundwater levels (including a check for leaking service pipes near the structure), and to confirm that the environment is that expected during the design or experienced in the earlier life of the basement. This may also avoid future disputes, by predicting the changes likely to occur after remedial work.

For Type A protection, where the internal environment relies solely on the integrity of the membrane (limited control), it is difficult to establish where failure of the membrane has occurred in relation to the ingress of water into the basement; i.e. water may travel between the tanking and the structure. In some instances the external wall membrane may be exposed locally for inspection by excavating outside the basement. It is rarely feasible to investigate the condition of an external floor membrane or its junction with the wall membrane. If an inaccessible external membrane cannot be economically repaired, alternative precautions will be required.

For Type B protection, if leakage results from deterioration of materials, the causes of the breakdown must be established so that they can be eliminated or taken into account during remedial work.

Drainage (particularly for Type C protection) will need to be inspected for blockage and adequacy.

The components of any active systems, e.g. pumps, heating systems, etc., should be checked to ensure they are functioning and have been maintained as specified.

5.2 MAINTENANCE OF THE INTERNAL ENVIRONMENT

When the defects in a basement make it unfit for its intended use, it is necessary to consider the extent and best method of repair. If, after investigation, extensive works are found to be necessary to return the basement to the required standard, it may be appropriate to consider improvement to a higher grade of internal environment. This is particularly so if the ingress of moisture is due to the progressive failure of an inaccessible membrane, or a change in the external environment such as rising groundwater levels or increases in hydrostatic pressure. The complete environmental control system of the basement should then be reassessed, disregarding any residual contribution from suspected deteriorating materials.

The effects of increased water pressure on the structure (due to the elimination of pressure relief by leakage) must be considered if work is to be carried out to make a wall or slab less permeable. This may affect the stresses, crack widths and deflections of the structural members together with the overall stability and factors of safety against flotation.

The selected method of repair must be compatible with the existing fabric, and tolerant of further changes in the environment where these are likely to occur. Examples of additional passive precautions available to maintain the internal environment are given in Table 5.1.

5.2.1 Repair methods

There is no simple universal solution to the problem of leakage through basements. Leakage may result from a number of causes, principally poor design and/or specification, defective materials, defective workmanship, deterioration of the structure, or a change in the external environment (e.g., rising groundwater or locally leaking sewers or water mains). Adjacent construction works may also affect the pattern of groundwater flow and surface water run off. A number of these factors may combine to cause problems.

The owner/occupier of the leaking structure has three basic options:

1.   Stop the ingress of moisture through the structure (improved passive precautions).
2.   Accept the leakage and identify the extra potential from heating and ventilation, drain or pump away (improved active precautions, see Section 3.9).
3.   Stop the water reaching the structure by lowering the water table locally or by pumping (improved active precautions).

The use to which the structure is put, the effect of leakage, the effect of de-watering on other structures and the relative cost of the options will generally determine which choice is made.

Should the decision be taken to stop the leakage (improved passive protection), the type and condition of the structure, the quantity of water entering, together with the hydraulic pressure on the structure, will generally determine the type of treatment undertaken. There is, however, often more than one technique that could be used in any particular instance, and numerous proprietary products are available for use. In many cases the choice of treatment is the result of a subjective rather than an objective review of the situation, and often reflects specific personal experience. This can produce an unsatisfactory end result because a particular technique, or material, which may have proved successful in one situation may be ineffective in another.

The passive precautions, referred to in (1) above can be grouped as follows:

■   reduction of the quantity of water entering the structure
■   improvement to the water-resistance of the structure
■   construction of a drained cavity.

Within each of these three groups there are a number of choices available to the designer. The methods available to *prevent moisture ingress* include:

Table 5.1   Examples of passive precautions available to achieve the required grade of internal environment in an existing basement

Existing basement depth and construction method	Target internal environment for an existing basement (of lower grade)			
	Grade 1 (basic utility)	Grade 2 (better utility)	Grade 3* (habitable)	Grade 4* (special)
	Limited environmental control Possibly adequate			*Complete environmental control* Normally required
SHALLOW (assumed no hydrostatic pressure, i.e. groundwater level below basement floor or drainage provided) likely to be residential **Masonry, reinforced masonry, plain or reinforced (precast or in-situ) concrete or steel sheet piling**	Grade not usually acceptable for residential basements General repairs at identified sources of leakage. Additional precautions may not be necessary	Specific repairs to identified defects Internal tanking (Type A) *or* drained cavity (Type C) protection	Specific repairs to identified defects Drained cavity (Type C) protection Passive precautions alone are not likely to be sufficient	If grade required the methods and precautions for shallow basements with permanent hydrostatic pressure should be followed
SHALLOW (with permanent hydrostatic pressure) **Masonry, reinforced masonry, plain or reinforced (precast or in-situ) concrete or steel sheet piling**	General repairs at identified sources of leakage. Additional precautions may not be necessary	Specific repairs to identified defects Internal tanking (Type A) *or* drained cavity (Type C) protection	Specific repairs to identified defects Excavation of surrounding ground (to walls) external tanking (vapour barrier Type A) protection ------------------------ External drainage, internal drained cavity (Type C) with a vapour barrier (Type A) protection	Specific repairs to identified defects Excavation of surrounding ground (to walls) external tanking (vapour barrier Type A) protection ------------------------ External drainage, internal drained cavity (Type C) with a vapour barrier (Type A) protection Passive precautions alone are not likely to be sufficient
DEEP (with permanent hydrostatic pressure) **Reinforced concrete including piled or in-situ perimeter wall**	General repairs at identified sources of leakage possibly sufficient Internal tanking (Type A) protection *or* drained cavity (Type C) protection likely to be necessary	Specific repairs to identified defects Internal tanking (Type A) *or* drained cavity (Type C) protection	Expensive to achieve for residential/office use Specific repairs to identified defects Internal drained cavity (Type C) with a vapour barrier (Type A) protection Passive precautions alone are not likely to be sufficient	Difficult to achieve and only at high cost Specific repairs to identified defects Internal drained cavity (Type C) with a vapour barrier (Type A) protection Passive precautions alone are not likely to be sufficient

*   Consideration should be given to the compensating benefits of upgrading the provisions for heating and ventilation.

Note: The possible solutions, and their associated costs, will be dependent on the condition of the existing basement and the difference between its current environment and that required.

5.2.1.1 Reduction in the quantity of water entering the basement

(a)   Expose exterior of structure and provide, or repair, Type A protection (not possible for the underside of a floor slab).

If the location of the breakdown of an existing membrane can be established, it may be possible in some instances, where access is not a problem, to excavate locally, adjacent to the structure, to expose the membrane and carry out repairs. Additional layers may be added to an existing tanking system or a new tanking system installed where it is possible to excavate all around the basement. Materials that have been applied successfully are essentially the same as those used in new construction (see Section 7.3), and include:

- mastic asphalt
- bonded preformed sheet membranes
- unbonded preformed sheet membranes (not suitable for local repair)
- liquid membranes
- water-resistant cementitious renders and polymer/cement coatings.

(b)   Tanking to the internal surface of the basement.

Where access to the external surface is not possible and water is thought to be travelling beneath the surface of an existing membrane or is entering the basement at a large number of points, i.e. where local repair is thought to be uneconomic, the use of internal tanking should be considered. This would require that the whole surface of the walls/floor of the basement be coated to prevent water from bypassing locally coated/repaired areas and entering the basement through adjacent defects. The base slab can also be made watertight by these methods in association with an external membrane applied to the walls. The materials that have been used are as above (see also Section 7.3). Where sandwich tanking is contemplated, sufficient loading coat must be applied to prevent debonding of the membrane.

Tanking both internally and externally is frequently used to upgrade the passive precautions of a basement, and additional details of their use are presented in Section 5.3.1.

(c)   Pressure or vacuum grout local cavities in the structure or subsoil at the back of the structure.

Grouting to cut off seepage is usually undertaken to repair isolated defects in the passive precautions. Where a large number of defects occur it would probably be more effective to prevent ingress by other methods. There are a number of types of proprietary grout materials available for use based on:

- cement
- bentonite
- chemical (silicates and acrylic)
- resins (epoxide, polyester and non-expansive polyurethane)
- expansive polyurethane
- modified rubber latex.

Grouting requires that holes be drilled through the walls/floor of the basement adjacent to the defect (sometimes inclined to intersect leakage paths) and the grout pressure or vacuum driven into the material behind, where it gels, sealing the leak. Grout selection and application are specialised techniques and advice from manufacturers and experienced applicators should be obtained prior to use. Often more than one phase of grouting may be needed as the leakage may be moved to defects elsewhere in the structure or higher up in the walls.

Care should be taken when grouting larger areas to ensure that any external drainage systems are not blocked.

5.2.1.2 Improvement in the water resistance of the structure

These techniques are particularly applicable to new construction using Type B protection where the required internal environment has not been fully achieved at the construction stage. They are generally used for repair while water is entering the basement.

(a)   Cut out defective material and make good.

Where a relatively small number of well-separated defects in the basement walls or floors result in leakage (e.g. poorly compacted concrete at kickers) adequate repairs may be achieved by cutting out and replacing the defective area (see Figure 5.1). Achieving a water-resistant joint between the substrate concrete and the repair material is the most critical feature of this method. The installation of temporary drainage points, in the area to be repaired, may be necessary in some situations to control the leakage. Some proprietary repair materials are however, formulated for application where running water is present.

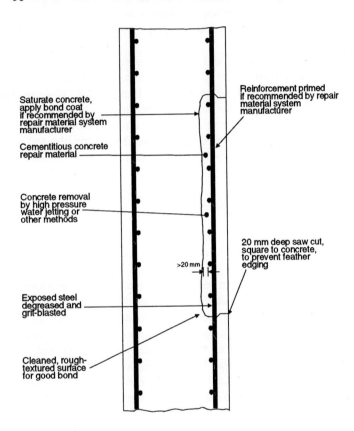

Figure 5.1 Structural repair of reinforced concrete using concrete repair system

Surface preparation and the compatibility of the physical and chemical properties of the repair material are important. Water jetting for concrete removal will prevent microcracking and loosening of exposed aggregate in the substrate, which often occurs with percussive techniques and results in poor bond. Many types of proprietary and non-proprietary repair materials are available, including:

■   concrete compatible with that used in the original construction
■   polymer-modified cementitious mortars and concrete
■   polymer-based mortars
■   sprayed concrete.

The properties of the repair material should match the substrate as closely as possible, particularly the shrinkage and thermal behaviour[5.2]. Specialist advice should be obtained to select the most suitable concrete repair system and to specify the required performance of the material to suit the size, depth and location of the area to be repaired. Polymer-based mortars are frequently specified for their increased water-resistance; however, other properties of the system, particularly shrinkage, may result in breakdown of the bond with the substrate and make them unsuitable for long-term use. Where proprietary mortars or concretes are to be used, they should always be applied in accordance with the manufacturer's instructions, and any repair should be undertaken by experienced contractors. Close supervision will be required to ensure that repairs are carried out adequately.

(b)   Filling cracks and porous parts of the structure by pressure or vacuum injection.

This technique has been used successfully to seal cracks and joints, particularly at kickers where a waterstop has become displaced and cutting out and replacement is not practical. Porous areas of concrete can sometimes be injected successfully, but severe honeycombing should always be cut out and replaced.

Crack or joint filling should only be undertaken where no further movement, through structural loading or thermal effects, is likely to take place. This provision does not apply to porous areas of concrete. Further movement is more likely to take place in newly constructed basements that have only been in service for a short period, i.e. approximately six months, and which have not reached equilibrium. Where a basement environment must be Grade 3 or 4, and immediate occupancy is required, this delay may not be acceptable, and a grout must be selected that can accommodate a small degree of movement. Materials which could then be used include:

- epoxide resin
- polyurethane resin
- polyester resin
- SBR and acrylic emulsions
- polymer-modified cementitious grouts.

Injection techniques have been used to seal cracks with widths down to 0.1 mm. It is unlikely that grout will fully penetrate cracks with widths less than this, particularly if they are bifurcating, owing to the presence of moisture or trapped air. Few resin-injection systems will displace water in a crack, joint or void, or cure in the presence of moisture. Where the wall or floor is expected to remain damp a water-tolerant grout such as water-based epoxide resin should be used. In general, crack sealing to reduce water penetration is not intended to restore the structural performance of a wall or floor. Where non-structural crack sealing is required a latex emulsion may be used (though this will not be resistant to hydrostatic pressure). The selection of grout systems will therefore depend upon:

- the likelihood of structural movement
- the nature and size of defect
- the moisture content of the substrate
- the temperature of the structure
- the injection method to be used.

(c)   Sealing cracks and porous areas of the structure with resins or cementitious mortars.

If structural continuity is not required, and where there is no hydrostatic pressure against the adhesion of the repair, cracks and porous areas can be sealed against the ingress of moisture by brushing cement or neat cement grout, or low viscosity latex emulsion into them. As with (b) above, the cracks should be static. Generic groups of suitable materials include:

- cementitious slurry
- cement/silica fume slurry
- polymer-modified cementitious slurry
- polymer resin
- crystal growth materials
- epoxide putty.

5.2.1.3   Construction of a drained cavity

> Where the points of leakage into a basement are extensive the most reliable and economic solution may be to construct a drained cavity (this should not however, be used to hide large inflows of water). Where this is the case, the work should be considered as an improvement in the grade of internal environment and as such, is considered in Section 5.3.2.

The above is a summary of the passive methods that could be used to improve water resistance. Each method requires specialist experience to specify and execute successfully. In a number of instances a combination of treatments may be necessary to prevent ingress through a structural element.

5.2.2   Active measures

Where improvement in, or installation of, active measures to control the internal environment is considered necessary the specialist advice of building services engineers is essential (see Section 3.9).

5.3   IMPROVING THE INTERNAL ENVIRONMENT

The moisture-resistance of an existing basement may be enhanced to provide a higher grade of internal environment. In this way basic utility, better utility or habitable grade basements may be improved to become habitable grade or special grade respectively. This section would also be applicable where an existing basement with no effective protection is to be upgraded to habitable grade or better.

The additional passive methods available to improve the control of the internal environment, examples of which are set out in Table 5.1, generally consist of:

- tanking, and/or

- the construction of a drained cavity.

Within each of these groups a number of different techniques are available. The option selected will depend on a number of features including the client's requirements, the likely groundwater level, access to the exterior of structure, cost, etc. An investigation of the current condition of the structure (as described in Section 5.1) should establish the possibilities for upgrading.

The options for improving the control of the internal environment by upgrading existing, or the installation of new, active measures are set out in Section 3.9. The advice of building services engineers will be required.

5.3.1 Tanked improvement

Tanking may be carried out either internally or, occasionally, externally to provide Type A protection. External tanking of walls may be possible in some shallow basements, but this will depend on whether excavation is feasible and the likely cost.

5.3.1.1 External tanking

It is sometimes possible to gain access to the exterior faces of the basement walls (by excavating alongside) to permit an external membrane to be installed. This would only be economic where the excavation is shallow. The membrane may be bonded or an unbonded hydrophilic variety (see Section 7.3), to minimise the passage of water between the face of the wall and the membrane. See Section 3.6.1. for details of external tanking systems. The membrane cannot be continued under the basement floor, which may require waterproofing by other techniques, which include grouting and internal tanking, as described in Sections 5.2.1 and 5.3.1.2, or the construction of a drained cavity floor (see Section 5.3.2).As in new construction the continuity of appropriate precautions from wall to floor must be provided.

Sandwiched tanking (see Section 3.6.3) may be provided by the construction of an external wall.

5.3.1.2 Internal tanking

It is sometimes more effective and economic, however, to improve the existing passive precautions of a basement by installing tanking on the inner face of the walls and floor.

Modified cementitious renders are particularly suitable for this type of application. Sandwich tanking with other forms of membrane may be used with the provision of a sufficiently thick loading coat. See Section 3.6.4 for details of internal tanking for new construction. The following points are particularly relevant to remedial work.

- Water-resistant render can be applied at any time during the life of the structure, and there is no requirement for external excavation, pumping or site drainage.
- Some renders can be applied in adverse site conditions, even where there is severe water ingress, as they do not require a dry surface to achieve good bond to the substrate and the ability to withstand high hydrostatic pressure (from behind) has been claimed (up to 80 m head in some cases).
- The thickness of an applied render is small (less than 20 mm) and it can be worked around corners, projections and openings without seams or joints. The floor screed can be overlapped to form a continuous layer within the basement.
- Membranes are vulnerable to mechanical damage and must be protected.
- Water-resistant render relies on its mechanical bond with a keyed surface to resist the hydrostatic pressure. Mesh or other supplements to the bush-hammered or grit-blasted concrete substrate may be required. Surface preparation must be carried out thoroughly.
- All existing fixtures and fittings must be removed to permit installation, including joinery, electrical fittings and surface-mounted pipework.
- Preparation and rendering work are wet trades.
- Future installation of fixings after application of waterproof render requires care to ensure it is not damaged. Lightly loaded fittings can be mounted directly onto the render or onto pads using suitable adhesives.
- Future penetrations require specialist making good of the render around the opening.
- No protection from external contamination is afforded to the structural elements.
- The render is hand- or nozzle-applied and is only as good as the applicator.

5.3.1.3 Reverse tanking

Reverse tanking applied to existing floors requires an overlay concrete or screed for protection. The tanking being an impermeable material, the moisture content of the concrete below it will normally rise above the air-dry condition as moisture is sealed in. This is not necessarily a problem if:

■   the ground-supported floor is covered with an impervious material, e.g. membrane
■   no organic material that can decay is in contact with the floor
■   no visible deterioration of the concrete has been observed over several years
■   there is no route for dampness to reach the walls.

If the moisture content becomes higher, the bond between layers may not be sufficient to resist any vapour pressure developed, which could lead to lifting of the screed/linoleum/tiles.

5.3.2 Improvement by drained cavity

The construction of a drained cavity (including the addition of a drained floor, where sufficient headroom exists) is likely to be required where the basement is to be upgraded to a Grade 3 or 4 internal environment. It may also be the most economical method of achieving or maintaining the required grade of environment in a basement where substantial leakage has been experienced. The principal features of construction are as for new construction described in Section 3.8.

As with new construction, both traditional internal wall construction (masonry etc., see Section 7.2) or proprietary drainage systems (see Section 7.7) may be used. The latter may be more advantageous with regard to the ease and speed of construction, as they can be used for both walls and floors. They may also act as a vapour barrier where the joints are sealed, and there is also a lower space penalty. The following points should be considered, particularly for remedial work.

■   It allows the basement to be raised to a higher grade of internal environment.
■   It requires the provision of channels, sumps and drainage in excess of those likely to be present in the original basement. This may require piercing of the basement floor.
■   The cavity formed may require natural or mechanical ventilation.

5.3.3 Improvement by active measures

Where improvement of the internal environment by upgrading existing, or the installation of new, active measures is considered, the specialist advice of building services engineers is essential (see Section 3.9).

REFERENCES

5.1   BUILDING RESEARCH ESTABLISHMENT
       Damp proofing existing basements
       BRE Good Building Guide No. 3, 1993

5.2   JOHNSON, R.A., LEEK, D.S. and KING, E.S.
       Underground service reservoirs: Waterproofing and repair manual
       CIRIA, 1995

6   Water and vapour resistance of residential basements

6.1   INTRODUCTION

This chapter is specifically related to shallow basements and semi-basements for Grade 2 (better utility) and 3 (habitable) internal environments. It deals with the precautions for garages, games rooms, utility rooms, stores and living accommodation in residential basements for houses (with two or three storeys) on sites where gravity drainage to below the level of the basement floor can be consistently achieved and there is no appreciable risk of flooding. In these ground conditions it may not be necessary to incur the expense of some of the precautions discussed previously in Chapter 3.

On this basis it is possible to simplify the guidance given in respect of basement construction in such favourable conditions. This chapter therefore offers advice applicable to residential buildings intended to achieve the minimum requirements of the Building Regulations[6.1] for Grades 2 or 3 internal environments[6.2].

> Where external environments are not so favourable, basement design should follow the guidance for shallow basements given in Chapter 3.

Chapter 3 should also be consulted for larger, taller residential buildings or deeper basements and in all cases *'where the water table can rise to within 0.25 m of the lowest floor of the building, or where surface water could enter or adversely affect the building, then either the ground to be covered by the building should be drained by gravity or other effective means of safeguarding the building should be taken'*[6.1] for which a more sophisticated design process is envisaged.

BS8102: 1990[6.3] gives basic guidance applicable to residential basements which is expanded, in the following sections.

Key definitions relevant to this chapter, from Chapter 1, are summarised as follows:

Shallow basement	Not more than one storey wholly below ground level (see also Section 1.4.1).
Semi-basement	Single storey with only one wall fully or partially submerged below ground level.
Residential basement	A shallow or semi-basement providing space, as either storage and/or as accommodation, to part of the housing with which it is associated.
Cellar	Basement, or part of, used for storage, heating plant and for purposes other than habitation (following definition in BS6100: 1984).

The Building Regulations 1991[6.1] definition of a basement is as follows:

Basement	*'a storey of which the floor is at any point more than 1.2 metres below the finished surface of the ground adjacent to it'.*

6.1.1 Residential basements: The benefits

The construction of basements in new houses and the improvement of existing basements can provide a more efficient use of buildings, particularly on sloping sites. This is advantageous where space is limited, land costs are high or there are planning constraints on the 'footprint' or height of buildings.

The additional space provided by basements is easy to insulate and provides thermal capacity for the building as a whole as well as valuable space for storage, heating equipment, recreational activities and other habitation uses detailed in Section 6.2.1.

Basement construction was commonplace in the nineteenth century, but much has proved troublesome owing to water penetration. There are no greater practical difficulties in constructing basements in the UK than elsewhere. The problems of preventing moisture ingress can be resolved in the UK as easily as they are in Europe, North America and Scandinavia, where basements are commonplace.

A report of a study[6.4] for shallow and semi-basements provides cost estimates of using in-situ concrete or reinforced masonry as the principal construction material, and the costs of different waterproofing methods for alternative housing types (detached, semi-detached and terraced). Additional costs are also given for the development of waterlogged sites.

6.1.2 Residential basements above drained groundwater level

Shallow basements constructed wholly or partly below ground level (i.e. a semi-basement) and above groundwater level, and basements where the groundwater level is controlled by drainage, are both considered in this chapter. Such basements could provide the full range of residential uses including living space, garages, games rooms, utility rooms and stores. The simplest provision is for houses, with two or three storeys above ground, on sites where gravity drainage to below the level of the basement floor can be consistently achieved and where there is no appreciable risk of flooding. This will generally only apply to sloping sites, where at least part of one wall of the basement will be above ground level.

On sloping sites, where cut-off drains are provided, no sumps or pumps are expected to be required and the risks of water penetration are significantly reduced. Drained floors are also not normally required. The Building Regulations Approved Document B[6.1] recognises the necessity to provide safeguards for fire safety in semi-basements by providing doors and windows on at least one external wall 'to give opportunity for smoke venting and fire fighting'. In other cases and with larger structures, more than one staircase is required for habitable basements.

6.1.3 Water- and vapour-resisting precautions for residential basements

In the UK, no matter how dry the soil around a building appears to be, there will still be some moisture in the ground, even if it is well above the water table. This moisture will generally be supplemented by rainwater soaking into the ground either directly or from soakaways and drains. Unless precautions are taken to prevent it, moisture will migrate from the surrounding ground through the walls and floor of the basement by a combination of flow under pressure, capillary action and water vapour transfer.

The decision as to whether shallow basements above drained groundwater level need, or can rely on, integral protection provided by the structural elements is determined principally by the intended use.

The decision will also be influenced by other aspects of the external environment as well as the proposed construction methods and materials. Once the required internal environment has been classified (see Tables 6.1, 2.1 and 2.2), appropriate measures to control moisture movement can be achieved by a combination of:

- drainage of the ground to control the water table
- total or partial barriers to resist moisture ingress (see Sections 3.3.3 and 3.6)
- sufficient ventilation and drainage to match the maximum degree of moisture ingress and to maintain the required relative humidity for the intended use (see Section 3.9).

As the BRE Construction Guide[6.5] to damp-proofing basements states: *'although it is technically possible to damp proof any structure, even those at high risk from dampness or flooding, the cost of work escalates rapidly with increasing complexity'*. For this reason a simple and reliable approach to residential basement construction is necessary; in some applications a degree of vapour ingress may have to be tolerated. Where this is the case, compliance with the Building Regulations may be achieved by the use of adequate heating and ventilation as established by a DoE determination[6.6]; see also Section 3.4.1.

Significant amounts of moisture may be generated in a basement when, for example, it contains bathrooms, utility rooms for laundry, or when warm damp air is vented into a cooler basement. The objective should be to exclude moisture from the basement in order to maintain, with appropriate ventilation, the internal environment suitable for its intended use. This chapter describes where the following precautions may be appropriate:

- drainage, or other means, to maintain groundwater (and flood water) below the level of the top of the basement floor slab
- moisture-resistant barriers in the basement floor slab
- moisture barriers to walls
- ventilated cavity construction for any inhabited rooms within the overall basement.

6.2 REQUIREMENTS FOR NEW AND EXISTING BASEMENTS ABOVE DRAINED GROUNDWATER LEVEL

Water resistance is a general requirement of all new basements and the improvement of existing basements. The broader objectives of basement design include the following:

1. To provide the occupier with:

- an acceptable layout for the intended use
- an acceptable internal environment for the intended use
- a means of safe escape in the event of fire.

2. To provide adequate:

- drainage (to avoid high groundwater levels)
- mass or other precautions (to avoid flotation during construction)
- load transfer from higher storeys to the ground
- foundations
- walls and floors with respect to structural loads and soil pressure
- ventilation
- allowance for likely structural movements.

3. To provide a low-maintenance durable structure:

- by using durable materials
- by excluding harmful substances both from the interior of the basement and from the structure itself.

6.2.1 Internal environments (grades) for particular uses

A designer must first define, through discussions with the client, the required internal environment for the basement or parts thereof. For the purposes of this chapter, which seeks to simplify the guidance relevant to many residential basements, a Grade 3 (habitable) environment is assumed to be the most likely to be specified as described below. In some circumstances the application associated with residential construction may need to conform to a lesser or higher grade.

It is most important that the initial investigation of ground conditions and the assessment of the required internal environment is carried out with accuracy, as over-specification may incur unnecessary expense and under-specification could result in expensive upgrading work (if indeed such work is feasible).

Maintaining the internal environment in the face of present, as well as future external environmental conditions, may depend to a considerable degree on the design of the active precautions (heating and ventilation). Detailed and accurate site investigation reports of adjacent structures and services are essential in predicting future ground conditions as well as in evaluating appropriate forms of construction.

Regardless of the intended internal environment, some forms of construction may not be adequate without tanking if particularly aggressive ground conditions exist. The provision of an impermeable membrane may therefore be necessary solely to protect the structure, or to prevent harmful substances from entering the basement.

Where the basement walls and floor, or basement floor only, are subject to hydrostatic pressure the guidance in Chapter 3 should be referred to. The four grades of internal environment are described in detail in Chapter 2 and BS8102: 1990. Appropriate precautionary measures and construction types, as described in the British Standard, are reviewed in Table 6.1.

Grade 3 will be appropriate for habitable rooms in residential basements. Grade 2 will normally be adequate for garages, stores and utility rooms. Grade 1, which permits 'some seepage and damp patches', is not normally acceptable for a residential basement.

> For rooms that may be inhabited in the future, provision for a Grade 3 internal environment is advisable.

Where a basement has some inhabited rooms and store rooms or a garage, it may be simpler and more economic if the whole of the basement is constructed to provide a Grade 3 environment. The option of providing drained cavity construction, as secondary protection, for the inhabited space within an otherwise Grade 2 environment may also be considered.

The essential distinction between these environmental grades is that Grade 3 requires a higher level of vapour resistance to minimise the risk to health.

Table 6.1   Guide to level of protection to suit basement use (based upon BS8102: 1990, this table adds descriptions to each grade reference and a commentary on the requirements)

Grade of basement	Basement usage	Performance level	Form of protection	Commentary
Grade 1 (basic utility)	Car parking; plant rooms (excluding electrical equipment); workshops	Some seepage and damp patches tolerable	Type B. Reinforced concrete designed in accordance with BS8110	Groundwater should be checked for chemicals which may have a deleterious effect on the structure, membrane or internal finishes
Grade 2[1] (better utility)	Workshops and plant rooms requiring drier environment; retail storage areas	No water penetration but moisture vapour tolerable	Type A Type B. Reinforced concrete designed in accordance with BS8007	Particularly careful supervision of all stages of construction is necessary Membranes can be applied in multi-layers with well lapped joints
Grade 3[2] (habitable)	Ventilated residential and working areas including offices, restaurants etc., leisure centres	Dry environment	Type A Type B. With reinforced concrete designed to BS8007 Type C. With wall and floor cavity and DPM	Groundwater should be checked for chemicals which may have a deleterious effect on the structure, membrane or internal finishes
Grade 4 (special)	Archives and stores requiring controlled environment	Totally dry environment	Type A Type B. With reinforced concrete designed to BS8007 plus a vapour-proof membrane Type C. With ventilated wall cavity and vapour barrier to inner skin and floor cavity with DPM	As Grades 2 and 3

Notes:

The shaded panels are particularly relevant to this chapter.

1 Cellars (see Section 1.4.1), etc. may be constructed to Grade 2.
2 Grade 3 is a minimum standard for habitable residential basements (see Section 6.2.1).

The recommendations in this table for 'Form of Protection' are identical to those of BS8102: 1990 *'Form of construction'*. These take no account of the groundwater table (high or low) or whether the soil is permeable or impermeable.

6.2.2 Investigation

A thorough site investigation should be carried out to determine the likely range of groundwater levels. The potential for drainage around the basement to prevent ground and flood water levels rising above the top of the base slab and the effect of such drainage on surrounding properties needs to be established. Unless the drained groundwater level is reliably below the level of the base slab, this simplified approach will not be appropriate. The chemical composition of the groundwater (see Chapter 2), the presence of other potentially deleterious materials from made ground, the possible temporary rise of ground or flood water during storm conditions (including the effect of drains and soakaways from adjacent properties), together with the risk of leakage from adjacent sewage or gas pipes etc., should also be assessed. The local authority should be consulted with respect to records and ground conditions at an early stage. They may have special requirements relating, for example, to methane gas migration from former refuse disposal sites and radon gas activity from some soils and rocks.

6.2.3 Passive precautions for residential basements in drained ground

On sloping sites, complications arise where houses are stepped in section and/or staggered in plan (see Figures 6.1 and 6.2). The solid separating wall between houses may require re-evaluation if it offers inadequate water and vapour resistance for the required internal environment where it becomes an external wall, or where the specification of masonry fails to meet thermal requirements. The external and internal wall/floor junctions are critical, requiring very careful design, specification and construction if moisture penetration is to be avoided[6.2]. Typical design solutions are given in Figure 6.3.

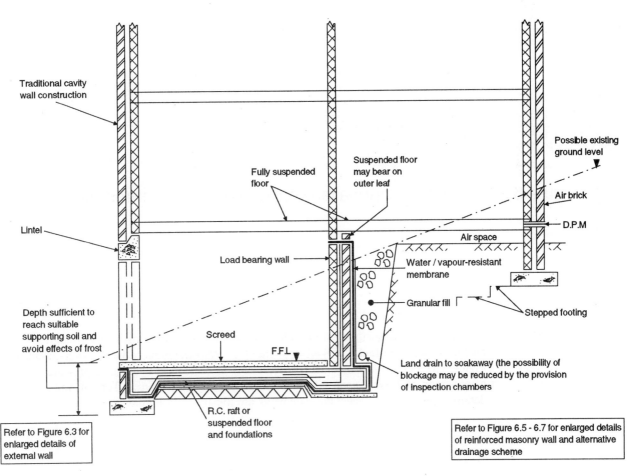

Figure 6.1 Typical reinforced masonry semi-basement water-resisting construction

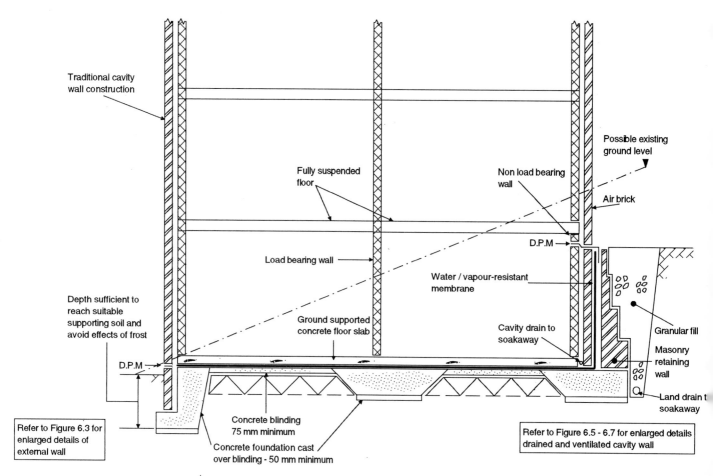

Traditional cavity wall construction

Possible existing ground level

Fully suspended floor

Non load bearing wall

Air brick

D.P.M

Load bearing wall

Water / vapour-resistant membrane

Depth sufficient to reach suitable supporting soil and avoid effects of frost

Ground supported concrete floor slab

Cavity drain to soakaway

Granular fill

Masonry retaining wall

D.P.M

Land drain t soakaway

Refer to Figure 6.3 for enlarged details of external wall

Concrete blinding 75 mm minimum

Concrete foundation cast over blinding - 50 mm minimum

Refer to Figure 6.5 - 6.7 for enlarged details drained and ventilated cavity wall

Figure 6.2 Typical masonry walled semi-basement water-resisting construction

The three principal methods of providing suitable protection against moisture ingress in basements are classified by Figure 6 of BS8102: 1990 (reproduced here with a commentary as Figure 6.4). For shallow basements subject only to occasional hydrostatic pressure, a combination of Type A and/or Type C protection may be preferred. Typical wall construction details appropriate to residential basements are illustrated in Figures 6.5-6.7.

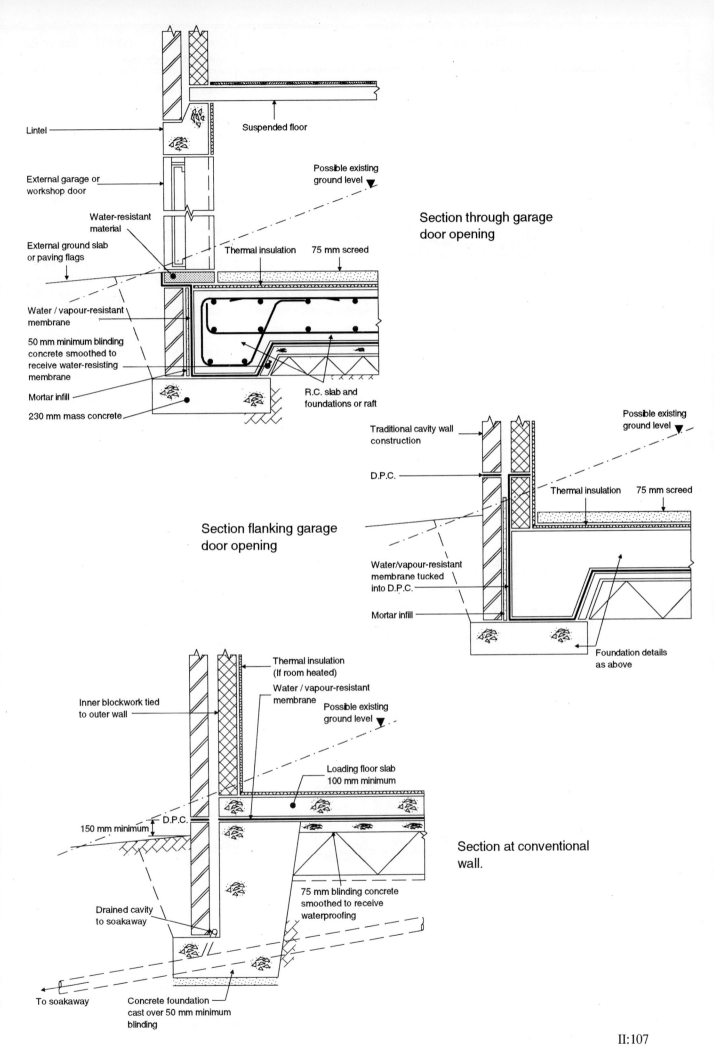

Lintel

External garage or
workshop door

Water-resistant
material

External ground slab
or paving flags

Water / vapour-resistant
membrane

50 mm minimum blinding
concrete smoothed to
receive water-resisting
membrane

Mortar infill

230 mm mass concrete

Suspended floor

Possible existing
ground level ▼

Thermal insulation   75 mm screed

R.C. slab and
foundations or raft

**Section through garage
door opening**

**Section flanking garage
door opening**

Traditional cavity wall
construction

D.P.C.

Possible existing
ground level ▼

Thermal insulation   75 mm screed

Water/vapour-resistant
membrane tucked
into D.P.C.

Mortar infill

Foundation details
as above

Inner blockwork tied
to outer wall

Thermal insulation
(If room heated)

Water / vapour-resistant
membrane

Possible existing
ground level ▼

Loading floor slab
100 mm minimum

D.P.C.

150 mm minimum

Drained cavity
to soakaway

**Section at conventional
wall.**

75 mm blinding concrete
smoothed to receive
waterproofing

To soakaway

Concrete foundation
cast over 50 mm minimum
blinding

II:107

Figure 6.3 Residential basements - typical wall / floor junctions

After Figure 6 from BS8102	Commentary on BS8102 to clarify the approach of the report

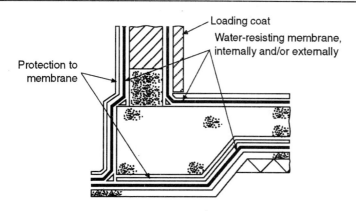

'Type A (Tanked protection). The structure itself does not prevent water ingress. Protection is dependent on a total water or water and vapour barrier system applied internally or externally'

Type A (Tanked protection)

Although not shown, external tanking, internal tanking or sandwich tanking is likely to be required for Grade 3 and 4 internal environments

The structural wall may be plain or reinforced concrete or masonry (brick or block)

Note: Neither a water-resistant nor a vapour-resistant barrier are necessary for Grade 1 (basic utility) or Grade 2 (better utility) internal environments

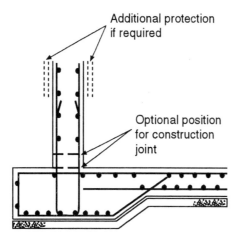

'Type B (Structurally integral protection). Example of detail of a concrete structure designed in accordance with BS8007 to be waterproof but not vapour proof. An external or internal vapour proof membrane could be applied'

Type B (Structurally integral protection)

Reinforced concrete structure designed and *constructed* in accordance with BS8007

(i.e. maximum calculated crack width of 0.2 mm)

Design to BS8110 or BS8007 does not, in itself, ensure fully water-resisting construction

To provide the vapour-resistance, requirements of some grades of internal environment external, internal or sandwiched tanking, or drained cavities may be added to the integral protection

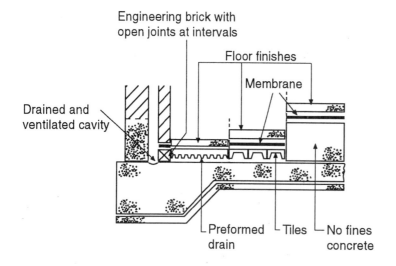

'Type C (Drained protection). The drained cavity wall and floor construction provides a high level of safeguard. Provision of a ventilated cavity and horizontal damp proof membrane prevents moisture ingress'

Type C (Drained protection)

External walls to be constructed as described in Type A or B above or to consist of other combinations described in previous sections of the report

The drained cavity (wall and floor) construction can be added to other precautions, Type A or B protection (or combinations of both) to provide the necessary level of water and vapour resistance

Figure 6.4: **Water and vapour protection classification (following the categorisation of BS8102: 1990).**
The above three categories of basic protection types may be used alone or in combination.

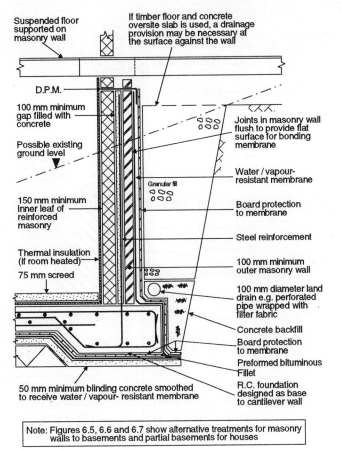

Suspended floor supported on masonry wall

If timber floor and concrete oversite slab is used, a drainage provision may be necessary at the surface against the wall

D.P.M.

100 mm minimum gap filled with concrete

Possible existing ground level

Granular fill

150 mm minimum Inner leaf of reinforced masonry

Thermal insulation (if room heated)

75 mm screed

Joints in masonry wall flush to provide flat surface for bonding membrane

Water / vapour-resistant membrane

Board protection to membrane

Steel reinforcement

100 mm minimum outer masonry wall

100 mm diameter land drain e.g. perforated pipe wrapped with filter fabric

Concrete backfill

Board protection to membrane

Preformed bituminous Fillet

R.C. foundation designed as base to cantilever wall

50 mm minimum blinding concrete smoothed to receive water / vapour- resistant membrane

Note: Figures 6.5, 6.6 and 6.7 show alternative treatments for masonry walls to basements and partial basements for houses

Figure 6.5 Residential basements: typical wall construction details

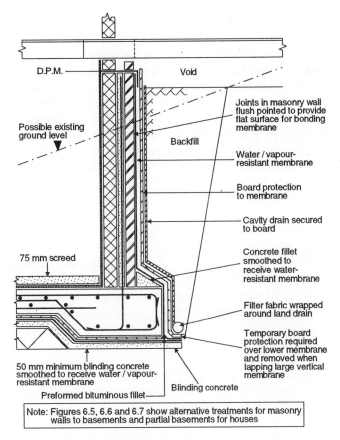

D.P.M.

Void

Possible existing ground level

Backfill

Joints in masonry wall flush pointed to provide flat surface for bonding membrane

Water / vapour-resistant membrane

Board protection to membrane

Cavity drain secured to board

75 mm screed

Concrete fillet smoothed to receive water-resistant membrane

Filter fabric wrapped around land drain

Temporary board protection required over lower membrane and removed when lapping large vertical membrane

50 mm minimum blinding concrete smoothed to receive water / vapour-resistant membrane

Preformed bituminous fillet

Blinding concrete

Note: Figures 6.5, 6.6 and 6.7 show alternative treatments for masonry walls to basements and partial basements for houses

Figure 6.6 Residential basements: typical reinforced masonry construction details; external cavity drain

II:109

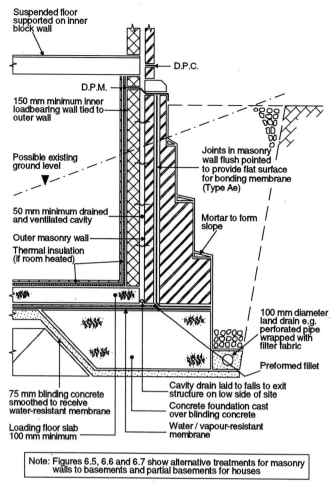

Suspended floor supported on inner block wall

D.P.C.

D.P.M.

150 mm minimum inner loadbearing wall tied to outer wall

Joints in masonry wall flush pointed to provide flat surface for bonding membrane (Type Ae)

Possible existing ground level

Mortar to form slope

50 mm minimum drained and ventilated cavity

Outer masonry wall

Thermal insulation (if room heated)

100 mm diameter land drain e.g. perforated pipe wrapped with filter fabric

Preformed fillet

75 mm blinding concrete smoothed to receive water-resistant membrane

Cavity drain laid to falls to exit structure on low side of site

Concrete foundation cast over blinding concrete

Loading floor slab 100 mm minimum

Water / vapour-resistant membrane

Note: Figures 6.5, 6.6 and 6.7 show alternative treatments for masonry walls to basements and partial basements for houses

Figure 6.7 Residential basements: typical unreinforced masonry construction details

6.2.3.1 Type A: Tanking protection

A continuous membrane is applied to the walls and floor of a basement to exclude water and/or vapour. This membrane may be placed either on the outer face (external), the inner face (internal) or within the thickness of the walls and floor (sandwiched, see also Section 3.6). There are many proprietary brands and types of membrane available (see Section 7.2), and a choice must be made from the appropriate materials to satisfy the thickness, grade and number of layers to be used in order that the required internal environment can be achieved. As drainage is expected to prevent exposure of the structure to a high, or constant, water pressure, wall membranes are expected to serve primarily as vapour barriers. In selecting the membrane, in addition to its moisture-resisting properties, its sensitivity to workmanship should also be considered, as future remedial works, if necessary, are likely to be costly.

Where tanked, the structure itself (which may be brickwork, blockwork or reinforced concrete) is not expected to resist the passage of water, as this is the primary function of the membrane. However, the structure must be capable of supporting the membrane effectively and must carry all the imposed loads including those resulting from earth pressure. Particular attention is required to the sensitivity of the membrane at construction joints: i.e. its capacity to bridge joints and accommodate cracking.

6.2.3.2 Type B: Structurally integral protection

Type B protection, as indicated in BS8102, is a reinforced concrete box, designed to BS8007 to resist hydrostatic pressure, vertical and horizontal loadings and also to prevent water ingress, but not water vapour transmission.

Preliminary design data for concrete used for residential basement walls are given in a BCA publication[6.7] with the intention of identifying where further work is required in order to promote basement construction in the UK.

Reinforced concrete for Type B protection requires specialist design and construction. Chapter 3 should be consulted for detailed guidance on this solution. The vapour permeability of concrete makes it necessary to consider whether the likely vapour gradient between the saturated soil, without hydrostatic pressure, and the internal environment is likely to be higher than can be accommodated by natural internal ventilation. Table 6.2 therefore makes a distinction between the capacity of Type B protection to safeguard Grades 2 and 3 internal environments, where drained cavities are not used.

Table 6.2   Assessment of the risk of failing to meet the criteria for water and vapour protection of new shallow basements and semi-basements above groundwater level

Protection type	Details of passive precautions	Internal environment	
		Grade 2 (better utility)	Grade 3 (habitable)
Type A	External tanked protection only (Concrete or masonry structures)	LL(r)	L(-)
Type B	Structurally integral protection only	LL(-)	L(v)
Type C	Drained protection only	Depends on external structure	
	Drained protection plus external tanking		LL(r)
	Drained protection plus sandwiched tanking		LL(r)

This table applies to shallow basements and semi-basements above groundwater level

Key:

Risk assessment

L   Low risk of inadequate water and vapour resistance (not dependent on heating and ventilation).

LL   Very low risk of inadequate water and vapour resistance (not dependent on heating and ventilation).

    (r)   generally appropriate
    (v)   generally requires a vapour barrier
    (-)   generally adequate

N.B.   The criteria for this assessment of risk is that any hydrostatic pressure is minimal and occasional, and that Grade 3 should have a vapour barrier (where this is not the case refer to Chapter 3

Construction types

Type A Concrete or masonry (brick or block) structures.
Type B Reinforced concrete (designed to BS8007 only).
Type C Concrete or masonry structures.

To ensure vapour resistance the Building Regulations, Approved Documents 1992[6.1], require a membrane to be included in concrete floor construction next to the ground, regardless of groundwater level. Also, a determination[6.6] has indicated that Type B protection would require the addition of a vapour barrier (either membrane or ventilated cavity) for a Grade 3 environment.

6.2.3.3 Type C: Drained cavity protection

Ventilated and drained cavities may be constructed within a basement wall and floor system where the resistance to moisture ingress of the structure and/or its tanking are insufficient to achieve the required internal environment. This form of protection (as shown in Figures 6.3 and 6.5–6.7) intercepts water that penetrates through the outer walls and floor. The cavity also prevents vapour transmission, provided it is adequately ventilated naturally to the open air or, if necessary, mechanically. The system acts in a similar way to that of a cavity wall above ground level. Water leaking into the cavity from defects, or condensation occurring in the cavity, is drained either to remote soakaways or surface water drains.

It is crucial with drained cavity protection that water is prevented from crossing the cavity via debris or wall ties. Access openings may be included for periodic cleaning of the drainage channels, and the provision and maintenance of ventilation in the cavities is important.

If the inner leaf of the cavity can be designed to be free-standing (i.e. without cavity wall ties) it is easier to keep the cavity clean during construction and maintenance. Where this is not possible, outward sloping stainless steel wall ties should be used to direct moisture outwards and reduce the risk of corrosion. Appropriate precautions should also be taken to exclude rodents from all cavities.

Where a cavity is not provided for the floor slab, Type A protection is frequently used. Special care is required at the junction of wall and floor membranes. Successful hybrid solutions of this type are difficult to achieve in practice, and Type C protection should be applied to both floor and walls if possible. This cavity can be formed in several ways; two options are shown in Figure 3.18. A DPM should be placed above every floor cavity (see Figure 6.4, Type C).

6.2.4 Strength and stability

The construction of residential basements may use either masonry (bricks or concrete blocks, plain or reinforced) or in-situ reinforced concrete or precast reinforced concrete panels or boxes. The British Standard documents appropriate to design and construction with the above materials are outlined in Section 3.4.3.

Perched water tables or natural groundwater levels occur close to the surface in many locations in the UK. If future groundwater levels rise, the pressure acting on basement walls and floors will increase. The possibility of uplift and increased horizontal pressures, even for relatively shallow basements, should be considered by the designer.

The drainage provisions at the time of construction must be checked to ensure that there is no risk of flotation, from flooding of excavations around the basement or from saturation of subsequent backfill, before the superstructure loads the basement. Flotation forces are generally high compared with the weight of a building, particularly during construction. If the development is 'low rise', normal residential construction loads may not be adequate to resist uplift under full hydrostatic pressure, and other measures may need to be taken to ensure that critical levels do not occur.

6.2.5 Active precautions (heating and ventilation)

Active precautions (heating and ventilation) may be specified to compensate for any water and vapour transmission into the basement in order to meet the requirements of the internal environment (as outlined in the Building Regulations 1991[6.1] and a determination by the DoE[6.6]).

The most appropriate passive precautions (Type A, B or C) will have been selected to achieve, as far as possible, the desired internal environment (Grade 1 to 4) in conjunction with the requirements outlined in Sections 6.2.1 to 6.2.4. The design of the active precautions for each basement will be unique, to suit the internal environment required and the probable vapour transmission of the passive precautions.

Evaluation of plant and ducting requirements must take account of the construction method, the size of the basement including individual rooms, as well as the emissions (gaseous and liquid) from any machinery, vehicles and/or human activity. Once the form of construction, dimensions and possible range of usage of the basement have been decided, it is essential to consult a building services engineer to establish the heating and ventilation options in relation to the passive protection measures.

General guidance on ventilation requirements and thermal transmittance (moisture transfer and condensation avoidance), related to heating and ventilation is given in Section 3.9. Worked examples of moisture and thermal transmission rates for residential basements are given in Appendix C.

Typical values for moisture loss, thermal transmittance and insulation of Type A and C protection for a Grade 3 residential basement are presented in Table 3.9.

Ventilation rates higher than the minimum derived from air change calculations (see Section 3.9) may be required to safeguard against condensation on cold walls. The risk of condensation on cold basement walls and floors may be greater than for rooms above ground[6.8–6.10]. Condensation may be reduced by the provision of ample ventilation preferably through high level vents, but in cold climates, where the basement is used as a habitable room (Grade 3 internal environment), this may not be feasible. In such instances it will be necessary to insulate the walls and floors, provide a vapour barrier on the warm side and supply heat to the basement. These provisions are comparable with measures which would be taken in above-ground rooms.

Ventilation of garage spaces must be sufficient to avoid concentrations of carbon monoxide.

6.2.6 Summary

Grade 2 internal environments in new residential basements above drained groundwater level require the prevention of water ingress, but some vapour transmission may be acceptable.

For Grade 3 environments a higher level of vapour resistance is required, principally for health reasons.

The selection of basement construction methods and materials and passive precautions will depend upon depth and the resulting wall pressure. Shallow or semi-basements, for low-rise buildings, are subjected to comparatively low loading, and when they are situated on sloping or easily drained sites the water table may remain below floor level. These situations arise most frequently in residential buildings requiring Grade 2 or 3 internal environments, and the use of the protection measures from BS8102 can be summarised as follows:

Type A: This is currently the most widely used water and vapour precaution for residential basements. Tanking is a precaution against moisture in the soil and against the occasional rise in groundwater. Tanking generally requires some protection from damage during backfilling. Masonry or boards may be used for this (see Section 7.8).

The use of external tanking is preferred, if site and design conditions permit, as the groundwater pressure forces the membrane against the structure. With internal or sandwiched tanking the converse occurs. Internal renders would not normally be recommended for new basements (see also Table 3.1) as they are unlikely to prevent vapour transmission.

Tanking systems are vulnerable, however, and the results of substandard workmanship can be almost impossible to rectify, owing mainly to the difficulty in locating the actual source of leakage if a moisture path exists behind the membrane.

Type B: Structurally integral protection in residential basements, as envisaged in BS8102, should be designed to BS8007 to resist any possible hydrostatic pressure and other loadings, and to minimise water and vapour ingress.

To conform with the simplified advice in Table 1 of BS8102 (see Table 6.1) it is possible to provide Type B protection alone to achieve a Grade 3 internal environment. However, the Building Regulations, Approved Documents 1992, require a membrane to be included in concrete floor construction next to the ground, regardless of groundwater level. A determination[6.6] has also indicated that active measures to control the moisture levels within a Type B protection basement would be sufficient for a Grade 3 environment.

Where hydrostatic pressure is minimal and/or occasional, the vapour resistance of structurally integral protection may be adequate for both Grade 2 and 3 internal environments. However, the specialist expertise required for construction is often considered by builders as a disincentive to using it (see also Sections 2.2 and 3.7 and Table 3.4). The addition of a vapour barrier for Grade 3 may also be considered necessary.

Structures with Type B protection may show some leakage initially, which for various reasons may reduce with time. However, it is usually possible to implement remedial action and deal with persistent local leakage (see Chapter 5).

Type C: Cavity drainage is generally considered to be a secondary precaution (it may not constitute vapour barrier alone) which, if care is taken to avoid blockage and exclude rodents, may be desirable for Grade 3 internal environments in combination with Types A or B protection. As the lining or inner leaf is accessible, this form of protection can be upgraded if its initial performance is found to be inadequate. Despite this, drained protection is not widely used for residential uses as it is difficult to avoid bridging the cavity, especially when an insulation layer is also required. When drained cavity protection discharges into the house drainage, without risk of back flow, or the introduction of odours or dangerous gases, it is an efficient system of protection. Guidance on drained cavity construction is given in Section 3.8.

6.3   TREATMENT OF EXISTING BASEMENTS

Where an existing basement does not adequately resist vapour or water transmission through the walls or floor, improvements may be required, either:

■   to achieve the intended internal environment, or
■   to raise the standard of the internal environment to a higher grade.

Detailed guidance on the methods and materials available is given in Chapters 5 and 7 respectively.

6.3.1 Overall review

The causes of the unacceptable environment must be established, including the following:

- damp and condensation which cause widespread problems in above-ground buildings exacerbated by the frequently colder, poorly ventilated conditions in basements
- a high water table
- occasional high water table after heavy rainfall
- leakage from adjacent damaged pipes
- permeable structural materials with a high water vapour transmission rate
- local defects, joints or cracks, acting as moisture paths
- leaking service pipes
- local breakdown of moisture barriers due to construction defects or ground movements.

6.3.2 Improvement of existing basements

The options for remedial upgrading (Section 5.3) of an existing basement are constrained by a number of factors. However, substantial improvements can be made by following the check-list from the overall review above and the broad principles set out in Chapter 5, which are summarised below:

- Upgrading the ventilation (either natural or by the introduction of active measures) is the only effective way to deal with condensation. It will also often be the simplest and most cost-effective method of dealing with small or moderate degrees of water vapour migration through walls.
- Improving thermal insulation may reduce the requirements for upgrading the ventilation. As in new construction, walls can be insulated externally or internally, providing a vapour barrier on the warm side. It is unlikely to be possible to add external insulation on the underside of a basement floor; therefore added insulation, superimposed over a vapour barrier, must be laid over the existing floor. Such insulation would then require the protection of a floating floor of timber or a fine concrete screed. This would result in a reduction of floor/sealing height.
- The potential for improved drainage around the structure, including weep-drains through walls, should be explored; however, the implications for the building and adjacent properties of a lowered water table must be considered.
- Improvements to flood drainage and drainage from rainwater downpipes may well be effective where occasional water ingress occurs.
- Damaged adjacent water services should be attended to. Particular care will be required, where sewers have been fractured, to remove contamination and avoid health hazards.
- Considerable improvements to permeable walls can be made by internal rendering or chemical injection. However, the effect on durability of a build-up of water pressure behind them must be considered when selecting appropriate materials.
- Specific leakage at defects can often be cured by a combination of drainage from behind and/or injection of local areas. Backfilled service trenches may, unintentionally, become french drains, directing a flow of water towards a basement wall.
- If leaking service pipes are suspected, excavation may be required to effect repairs, install new linings or lay new pipes.
- Breakdown of or defects in in-situ 'damp-proofing' materials can usually only be repaired by excavation around the basement[6.11].

The provision of internal drained wall and floor cavity construction provides a reliable method of substantially upgrading a Grade 1, leaking basement, to Grade 2 or 3, providing water can be reliably drained (e.g. to sumps for removal by pumping). However, there will be a loss of floor area and ceiling height using such measures.

REFERENCES

6.1   HMSO
       The Building Regulations 1991 (SI 1991 No. 2765) effective from 1 June 1992
       replacing The Building Regulations 1985 (SI 1985 No. 1065).

       The Building Regulations 1991, Approved Documents:

B2/3/4	Fire spread	1992 Edition
C1/2/3/4	Site preparation and contaminants	1992 Edition
C4	Resistance to weather and ground moisture	1992 Edition
D1	Cavity insulation	1985 Edition
F1	Means of ventilation	1995 Edition
F2	Condensation	1995 Edition
H1	Sanitary pipework and drainage	1990 Edition
H3	Rainwater drainage	1990 Edition
L	Conservation of fuel and power	1995 Edition
M	Access for the disabled	1992 Edition
Amendments		1992

6.2   DEPARTMENT OF THE ENVIRONMENT
       Personal communication

6.3   BRITISH STANDARDS INSTITUTION
       Code of practice for protection of structures against water from the ground
       BS8102: 1990

6.4   BRITISH CEMENT ASSOCIATION
       Options for quality in housing, Basements 1: Benefits, viability and costs
       BCA Report, 1991

6.5   BUILDING RESEARCH ESTABLISHMENT
       Damp-proofing basements
       BRE Good Building Guide No. 9, 1990

6.6   HMSO
       Determination C4, Whether the walls and floor would adequately resist the passage of
       water vapour
       Department of the Environment, Appeals and Determinations, June 1991

6.7   BRITISH CEMENT ASSOCIATION
       *Options for quality in housing, Basements 2 : A preliminary assessment of the design
       of basement walls*
       BCA Report, 1991

6.8   BUILDING RESEARCH ESTABLISHMENT
       Housing Defects Prevention Unit, Defect Action Sheets

       DAS 6:   External walls: reducing the risk from interstitial condensation, 1982
       DAS 16:   Walls and ceilings: remedying recurrent mould growth, 1983

6.9   BUILDING RESEARCH ESTABLISHMENT
       Rising dampness in walls: Diagnosis and treatment
       BRE Digest 245, 1981

6.10. HMSO
       Condensation in dwellings, Part 2 Remedial measures
       Department of the Environment, HMSO, 1971

6.11   NATIONAL HOUSE BUILDING COUNCIL
How to improve quality and prevent defects
NHBC, 1988

7 Materials

7.1 MATERIALS IDENTIFIED

The materials specified for water-resistant basement construction and passive protection systems will depend on the required internal environment (defined and quantified in Section 2.2), the nature of the external environment (Section 2.3), the construction method selected (Sections 3.3 and 3.4) and the passive precautions adopted (Sections 3.5 to 3.8).

The materials able to provide resistance to the passage of moisture referred to in this chapter are:

- *Structural Materials*

  1. Concrete - reinforced, prestressed, mass and sprayed, in walls, floors and piles
  2. Steel - piles and reinforced concrete, walls, floors and piles
  3. Masonry - brick or block walls including mortar

- *Tanking materials*

  1. External tanking
     - (a) mastic asphalt
     - (b) bonded preformed sheet membranes (e.g. 'torched on', using a bonding compound, self-adhesive)
     - (c) unbonded preformed sheet membranes (e.g. barrier membranes, hydrophilic bentonite composites)
     - (d) liquid membranes
     - (e) water-resistant cementitious renders and polymer/cement-based coatings

  2. Internal tanking

     as above, except for hydrophilic bentonite composites

- *Waterstops*

  1. External
  2. Waterstops within the in-situ wall and floor

     - (a) barrier
     - (b) hydrophilic
     - (c) co-extruded
     - (d) post-grouted tubes

- *Joint fillers and sealants*

  1. joint fillers
  2. joint sealants
  3. preformed strip sealants

- *External drainage systems*

- *Internal drainage systems*

- *Protection boards*

Materials within each group can be described in generic terms. However, the performance of materials even within the same generic group may vary widely.

7.2 STRUCTURAL MATERIALS

The choice of materials for the structural elements of the basement is dealt with in Chapter 3. Often they are used in combination. Factors that affect performance and durability are given below.

7.2.1 Concrete

The specification for concrete to achieve a required degree of water resistance will be dependent on the passive precautions type selected and the external environment (particularly the hydrostatic pressure) to which the concrete will be exposed.

Reinforced concrete can be used as the structural element associated with all three protection types (A, B or C). It is therefore possible to achieve any grade of internal environment (see Table 2.1 and 2.2) using reinforced concrete with, where necessary, suitable water and vapour protection (see Tables 3.1, 3.2 and 3.3).

Type A protection, to BS8102, requires no special measures with regard to the concrete materials (other than good mix design, workmanship and that the surface finish should be suitable for the application of the selected tanking system; i.e. the requirements of the tanking system will dictate the quality of the surface finish) while Types B and C protection may require the structural elements to be designed to BS8007 with additional design specification and construction precautions to control cracking and reduce permeability (see Section 3.7.2).

Structurally integral protection, Type B, requires reinforced concrete to be designed specifically to resist the hydrostatic pressure and other loadings, as well as to minimise water ingress. This relies on competent design and specification and the construction of high-quality, virtually crack-free, dense concrete to exclude water and reduce vapour transmission to an acceptable level. Concrete is not impermeable to water vapour and, in the limited cases where vapour transmission is totally unacceptable, supplementary active or passive protection must be provided.

The success of concrete in water exclusion will depend on three features:

- macro defects - cracks, opening joints, construction faults, etc.
- micro defects - microcracks, microporous zones, etc.
- the intrinsic porosity of the cement paste and aggregate.

Macro defects may not be accessible to view but can largely be eliminated by careful design of the structure and good site practices. Design for early thermal and flexural crack control is discussed in Section 3.7.2.1. It may be carried out in accordance with BS8110, maximum calculated crack width 0.3 mm or BS8007, maximum calculated crack width 0.2 mm, severe or very severe exposure, or 0.1 mm, critical aesthetic appearance, depending on the required internal environment and passive precautions selected. Crack widths can also be minimised by careful mix design and construction procedure. A summary of the factors that help to prevent or control early age cracking are given in Table 10 of CIRIA Report No. 91[7.1] and Concrete Society Technical Report 22[7.2]. The addition of ggbs and pfa to reduce the temperature rise of the hydrating concrete may also be possible and, if so, would be advantageous in this respect.

Other visible defects that occur in concrete (honeycombing, etc.) are primarily the result of poor workmanship. Congested reinforcement design may also be a contributing factor. Care needs to be taken to ensure accurate spacing and cover to reinforcement. Even distribution and adequate vibration of the concrete are essential.

Formed joints that are continuous through the concrete are an obvious weakness in the construction. It is essential that thorough surface preparation be undertaken to ensure good bond and to minimise leakage at the interface. If the structure is to be tanked there should be no differential movement at construction joints. This may require dowelled keyed joints to maintain the alignment of the adjoining structural elements. At designed movement joints additional precautions may be required (see Sections 7.4 and 7.5).

Micro defects, particularly microcracks, frequently occur as a result of the differential thermal properties of the constituents of the concrete, or tensile strains due to shrinkage, caused by rapid or differential drying out. These may be reduced by the selection of appropriate aggregates and adequate curing of the concrete.

All concrete will allow water vapour (and sometimes liquid) to pass through it, to some degree: minute quantities in the case of good-quality sound concrete subject to modest hydrostatic pressure. The extent of the permeability is governed by two factors: the permeability of the aggregates and the permeability of the cement paste. Most normal concreting aggregates are relatively dense and have low permeability: hence the majority of the overall permeability of concrete is due to the paste fraction. The porosity and permeability of the cement paste are principally controlled by the cementitious content and water/cementitious (w/c) ratio, which influences the size and distribution of void space due to free water, and, to some extent, by the paste density (crystal size composition and pore structure of the cement hydrates).

Correct aggregate grading can help to reduce the volume of the paste, hence reducing shrinkage. Reducing the w/c ratio, by the use of water reducing/plasticising admixtures, may result in desiccation of the paste and hence less permeable concrete. Curing, however, is of paramount importance in reducing the permeability of concrete by allowing the less finely ground cement particles to continue to hydrate and 'densify' the paste. It also has other benefits, such as reducing plastic shrinkage and its associated cracking.

There may be difficulty in achieving good adhesion between tanking materials or joint sealants and low-permeability concrete. The use of special primers and surface preparation may be necessary.

Ggbs and pfa used as cement replacements, which hydrate over long periods of time, also reduce the permeability of the concrete by blocking capillary pores, and encourage autogenous healing of cracks. Microsilica has also been reported to have beneficial properties in reducing the permeability of concrete[7.3]; however, there are currently no British Standards to assist in specifying its use in concrete, but an Agrément Certificate is available for a proprietary brand. It should however, be noted that the initial permeability of these concretes may be higher than most Portland cement only concretes (with an equivalent cementitious content). These concretes also require greater care to be taken during curing.

There are a number of commercially available 'waterproofing' admixtures for concrete, which are hydrophobic and work by repelling moisture; they may reduce moisture migration by interruption of capillary action. Most commonly available materials of this type are the calcium or ammonium salts of fatty acids such as stearates. Admixtures of this type may be effective in repelling surface water but are generally ineffective in reducing the passage of water under any sustained positive hydrostatic pressure[7.4].

Concrete for cast-in-place piles does not usually have to be high-strength, and the mix design and properties are constrained by the need to install reinforcement cages. Where soil or groundwater conditions are not aggressive, this has led to the use of mixes with low cement contents, containing plasticising and retarding admixtures to obtain the required workability and to minimise the heat of hydration (and hence shrinkage cracking) of the concrete. Mixes of this type will not, however, satisfy the durability requirements of BS8110 or BS8007, which are not intended for use in the design of piles.

Where secant piles, or diaphragm walls, are to be used to exclude external water, or in aggressive ground, the concrete mix should be designed to have similar performance to that required for structural-grade concrete designed to BS8110. The required workability may be achieved by the use of superplasticising admixtures. Thermal cracking may be minimised by the use of ggbs or pfa with the Portland cement.

Sprayed concrete, which may be used on the inside face of piled walls, can be made highly impermeable to the movement of water through it. Although the spraying operation generally traps a significant quantity of air (the total porosity is often higher than conventional concrete), the voids are non-interconnected and hence the permeability is generally low. Compaction may be difficult to achieve in some confined places, which would increase the permeability. The use of pfa and particularly microsilica is advantageous in reducing rebound and improving cohesion. Careful mix design and the use of admixtures can reduce the permeability of sprayed concrete to values lower than those obtained for conventionally placed high-quality structural concretes.

Plain (mass) concrete is confined to shallow basements, which can be constructed in an open excavation. It is not considered advisable to construct a water-resistant basement in plain concrete without tanking (Type A) or drained protection (Type C). Plain concrete basements are excluded from the BS8102 Type B (integral protection) classification.

Plain concrete construction is unlikely to be suitable for a Grade 4 internal environment, even with tanked and/or drained protection. This is due to the greater sensitivity of the structure to ground movement, or ground pressure, and consequently the greater risk of cracks too large for the passive precautions to deal with.

7.2.2 Steel

Continuous sheet steel is impermeable to the passage of water through it. Steel sheet piles are often used in basement construction as a method of ground support and temporary water exclusion. They may also be used as permanent formwork for concrete walls, where problems may occur if water leaks through the interlocking clutches and carries sediment onto wall kickers. Clutch-sealing compounds may be used to minimise this. Such compounds should not, however, be regarded as part of the permanent precautions.

Steel sheet piles with welded joints, to form a monolithic steel box, may be used in structurally integral protection (Type B). They should be watertight provided the individual sheets are undamaged during driving, the welding is fully continuous and the wall/floor junction can be sealed against hydrostatic pressure. The latter is likely to prove most difficult.

7.2.3 Masonry

Masonry walls can be used in association with Type A and Type C protection.

Advice on the use and durability of masonry components is given in BS5628. This code includes reference to the use of masonry below the level of the DPC and in below-ground environments, but in general deals with exposure conditions above ground level where durability is related to wind-driven rain. The degree to which masonry will become saturated below the level of the DPC. will depend on the site. Care should be exercised in the choice of materials to minimise water ingress in basement construction, even where additional precautions are to be specified. Combinations of masonry units and mortar types for the below-ground environment are specified in Table 13 of BS5628: 1985. Useful advice on treatments to increase water resistance is given in BS6477: Specification for water repellents for masonry.

Water can move through masonry by a number of mechanisms, including percolation under the action of gravity, evaporation and capillary suction.

There are three paths by which water can penetrate:

- through the masonry units
- through the mortar
- along the interface between the masonry units and the mortar.

7.2.3.1 Masonry units

There are a number of different types of masonry unit that have been used in basement construction. These include:

- clay bricks (to BS3921)
- calcium silicate bricks (to BS1887)
- precast concrete masonry units (to BS6073)
- reconstructed stone masonry units (to BS6457).

All masonry units are porous to some degree and will absorb and transmit water when they become saturated (water absorption is frequently used as a specification term for clay bricks). Some masonry units have impervious finishes to reduce or prevent water ingress; however, surface imperfections in these units may lead to saturation if the water is able to penetrate the finish by any path.

The principal factors affecting the durability, and hence water penetration properties, of masonry units are:

- Susceptibility to frost - this could occur in the upper section of a basement thermally insulated from the inside. Delamination of the surface of the unit reduces the length of the moisture path, and internal microcracking increases the rate at which moisture may penetrate.
- Salt crystallisation - salts from groundwater can crystallise at an evaporation front within the units, leading to cracking and moisture penetration.
- Aggressive groundwater - low pH groundwater, or waters with low levels of dissolved calcium, are particularly aggressive to concrete blocks and mortar.

7.2.3.2 Mortar

Mortars can be specified to provide a level of durability to match that of the bricks or blocks being used[7.5]. Types of mortars and their mix proportions are defined in Table 15 of BS5628: Part 3: 1985, which details mixes for increasing durability and resistance to penetration by water. Accuracy in batching and the type of mixer used are of particular importance in obtaining the required durability of the mortar. Site batching of constituents by volume (particularly when the method is by the 'shovel full') often leads to significant under-batching of cement, when compared with damp sand, and hence leaner mixes than intended are produced.

The factors that affect the durability of mortar are similar to those that affect concrete. Permeability is principally influenced by mix specification. Shrinkage of cement-rich mortars may result in cracking at the interface with the bricks and thus provide water paths. Sulphate attack is a major concern, with soluble sulphates originating from some clay bricks.

7.2.3.3 Joints (masonry unit/mortar interfaces)

Discontinuities or material interfaces are potentially the most likely features where moisture can penetrate. Masonry construction has a large number of such interfaces between the masonry units and the bonding mortar. Ideally the mortar, and its interface, should not be significantly more permeable than the masonry unit.

There are a number of features that may, however, affect the masonry/mortar adhesion and hence affect the permeability of the wall as a whole. These include:

■ Coefficient of thermal expansion - differential thermal movement (low except in semi-basements) of the masonry units and mortar can lead to stresses being generated, resulting in joint failure.

■ Dimensional changes in masonry units - some clay bricks may expand in certain circumstances, and concrete bricks and blocks shrink in drying conditions. Mixing clay and concrete masonry units in the same structural element should be avoided if possible.

■ High water absorption or dry masonry units with a high water absorption can 'suck' moisture out of the mortar, interfering with hydration at an important stage, leading to poor adhesion.

■ Chemical attack - chemical attack of mortar or masonry units can result in dimensional changes and loss of adhesion.

■ Drying shrinkage of the mortar - may cause it to de-bond from the masonry units.

BS5628 states that *'In cavity walls some water will inevitably penetrate the outer masonry leaf in prolonged periods of wind-driven rain'*. This is equally true for basement construction where the wall is exposed to groundwater.

Masonry construction is confined to shallow basements constructed in open excavation. Masonry walls should not be used as the primary waterproofing system in new basements. Their contribution is therefore limited to Type A or C protection.

Unreinforced masonry or plain concrete construction is unlikely to be suitable for a Grade 4 internal environment even with tanked and/or drained protection. This is due to the greater sensitivity of the structure to ground movement, or ground pressure, and the consequently greater risk of cracks too large for the passive precautions to deal with.

7.3   TANKING MATERIALS (INTERNAL AND EXTERNAL)

Tanking is the most commonly used method of increasing the moisture resistance of basement construction. It provides a physical barrier (membrane or render) on either the outside or, where appropriate, on the inside of the structure. Internal membranes require the support of a loading coat to resist the hydrostatic pressure, which tends to 'push' the membrane off the structure.

Type A protection may be adequate for Grade 1, 2 or 3 environments, but continuing good performance will depend on the tanking system's reliability, which is difficult to check either during, or after, construction. The likelihood of complete success may be influenced by difficult site application conditions and construction details inhibited by cost. In the event of failure of external tanking, it may not be possible to repair it, even if it is accessible, without finding the position of defects, as water is known to be capable of travelling under membranes not fully bonded to the structure to points remote from the entry. 'Water testing' the tanking[7.6] may be undertaken to check the integrity of the membrane prior to backfilling. The addition of drained cavities may be considered a desirable additional measure for Grade 3 and a necessary measure for Grade 4 environments, especially if high hydrostatic pressures are foreseen, (Sections 3.9, 7.2 and 7.7).

Tanking materials may need to withstand a number of forces during their service life, including:

1. Hydrostatic pressure - likely to vary during the life of the structure.
2. Dead loads from the structure - a membrane, particularly beneath the floor slab, may be required to transfer structural loads to the ground.
3. Disruptive forces caused by ground movement - which may vary during the life of the structure.
4. Forces generated by the structural materials to which the tanking is applied - movement due to expansion, or shrinkage, of construction materials may occur during the life of the structure. Such forces may disrupt or puncture the membrane and lead to water penetration sufficient to affect the internal environment adversely.

Tanking materials may also require a degree of chemical resistance against some aggressive external environments in order to continue to function effectively over their required service life.

Currently there are no methods of assessing the life of a material, other than by its previous in-service performance record, which may be relatively short in the case of new materials. The life expectation will depend on the conditions in service, and will vary with each application.

Where a basement relies entirely on tanking for its resistance to moisture penetration (Type A protection), the material will need to be reliably robust (particularly where hydrostatic pressure is encountered), owing to the high cost of remedial measures. The degree of protection provided by a tanking system is not, however, solely the result of the properties of the barrier material. Other features of the system are equally important, for example:

- Surface preparation: Masonry construction may require a modified render to provide a suitable surface.
- Application, particularly workmanship in the formation of many metres of lap joints.
- Feasibility and 'buildability' of design details, e.g. the production of intricate blinding profiles and the difficulties of adhering some types of membrane to them or complex overlap details.
- Openings for services: The membrane will need to be cut and the edges sealed where services must pass through the envelope (see Section 8.2), etc.

Joints (laps) between sheets and surface preparation of the substrate (the requirements for which vary with the type of membrane selected) are critical to the success or failure of the tanking operation. In many cases the 'waterproofing' of a basement has 'failed' not because of inherent faults in the material (relatively rare) but because of lack of attention to these other features of the system as a whole.

Consultation at the design stage between all parties concerned with the supply and installation of the selected tanking precautions is advantageous, and manufacturers' recommendations on the use of these materials should be followed.

The selection of a particular material should be based on its suitability for the particular application. Care should be taken to avoid materials incompatibility: for example, some elastomeric sealants are not compatible with bituminous membranes; soft membranes are not suitable for transmitting loads and should not pass through pile caps or column bases.

7.3.1 External tanking materials

External tanking materials are described below under five categories:

- mastic asphalt
- bonded preformed sheet membranes
- unbonded preformed sheet membranes
- liquid membranes
- water resistant cementitious renders and polymer/cement coatings.

Materials covered by British Standards are mastic asphalt and bituminous sheet membranes. Most other materials are British Board of Agrément certified.

7.3.1.1 Mastic asphalt

Mastic asphalt in accordance with BS6925 and BS6577 consists of graded minerals in an asphaltic cement to form a bitumen-saturated structure. It is a thermoplastic, applied hot without compaction, which when cooled should be able to accommodate a small amount of building movement, although it may embrittle with age and oxidation. In the solid state, free from voids, it should be impermeable to water, even under high hydrostatic pressure. It also has a very high vapour resistivity, of the order of 1100 GNs/kgm (the vapour resistance is proportional to the thickness of the layer, hence a 20 mm thick layer would have a vapour resistance of approximately 22 GNs/kg).

Comprehensive details of the application of mastic asphalt for the exclusion of water from basements are given in BS8102 and the Mastic Asphalt Procedures Association *Tanking handbook*[7.7], with workmanship aspects being covered by BS8000: Part 4: 1989. There are some points which should be noted, however:

- It is preferred for use in the external situation where any hydrostatic pressure will force the asphalt on to the substrate surface.
- It may embrittle and shrink over long periods of time, owing to oxidation, and there may be a slight deterioration in long-term adhesion to the substrate.
- It cannot accommodate cracks that may form in the supporting structure after it has been applied.
- Some concrete surfaces may need to be primed with bitumen emulsion to achieve good bond. (There is some confusion in the interpretation of BS8102 with regard to the use of emulsion-based primers in association with mastic asphalt. This report considers that they should only be prohibited in association with bituminous membranes; however, manufacturers should be consulted on their use with particular products).

7.3.1.2 Bonded preformed sheet membranes

Sheet membranes are preformed, factory-supplied in rolls, which are bonded together on site to form a continuous membrane by lapping. Application may be by a number of means including:

- Torching - some bituminous sheets are designed for application by torching, in which the surface of the membrane that is to come into contact with the structure is heated as it is unrolled. The degree of heating must be such as to form a continuous bead of molten bitumen, from the membrane, across the full width of the sheeting. Care is required to avoid overheating (scorching) of the sheeting as it is installed, as this may result in inadequate bond being achieved.

- Bonding compounds - a suitable grade of oxidised bitumen (85/25, 95/25, 105/35 or 115/15) is used as a hot-melt adhesive at an application rate of approximately 1 kg/m^2 to bond the preformed sheets together (in laps or multiple layers) and to the structure. The adhesive layers themselves add to the resistance to water transmission of the tanking membrane.

■ Self-adhesive membranes - rubber/bitumen sheets on a plastic carrier film or bitumen reinforced by a polymer fleece, backed with a pressure-sensitive adhesive, are commonly used. The bitumen forms the primary waterproofing layer. If the carrier film is lost or damaged the membrane still retains its water-resisting properties. Silicone paper or other non-stick materials are used as backing to prevent the membranes from bonding together prior to application.

Bonded membranes are sometimes difficult to handle on site, especially in restricted spaces and at 'three-cornered' junctions; complex structure geometries should be avoided if possible.

Surface preparation of the substrate is important for all types of bonded preformed sheet membrane (the actual requirements being system specific): for example, ensuring that it is sufficiently smooth to prevent damage to the membrane and has a sufficiently large bond contact area, that it has a suitably low moisture content (application requires dry conditions if adhesion problems are to be avoided) for bonding to be successful, and that it is structurally sound and hard (shuttering holes and cracks should be filled and allowed to harden prior to tanking). Some materials are more tolerant to site and construction conditions than others, but in general the sensitivity to surface imperfections increases as the total membrane thickness decreases.

All types of sheet are susceptible to aggregate penetration to some extent during backfilling, and should be protected by purpose-made boards or masonry.

Water transmission through all sheet membranes is low irrespective of type except where they are damaged or become debonded. In general the grade of sheet chosen will depend on the environment. BS8102 recommends at least two layers of fully bonded sheets. This may need to be increased in environments where high hydrostatic pressure is expected, and corners should generally be reinforced by the addition of extra layers. Design of the system (in terms of the number of layers required, simple easy-to-construct details, etc.) and the quality of workmanship during installation (ensuring high standards of surface preparation, good bond, adequate overlaps at joints, etc.) are of primary importance.

Some types of sheet material that have been 'stretched' by calendering (rolled to uniform thickness) during manufacture may undergo 'memory shrinkage' even after application, which may result in bond and/or joint failure.

Chemical resistance varies with composition; hence membranes should be selected with particular regard to the external environment. Organic solvents may cause softening, resulting in loss of water resistance of some membrane types. Some materials are particularly resistant; these include polymer plasticised PVC and polyethylene polymer sheets. All types of sheet are resistant to uncontaminated groundwaters.

Spillage of fuel, e.g. petrol or diesel (which is less reactive but does not evaporate as quickly), may cause damage to many types of membrane and should be prevented. Bituminous membranes are not fuel-resistant. The type of membrane to be used should be selected with respect to the quantity of fuel likely to be present in the environment, e.g. occasional accidental spillage or permanent contact from a fuel line.

Generic groups of bonded preformed sheet membranes are identified in Figure 7.1. The sheets may be categorised into bitumenised fabric, bitumen/rubber, polymeric, elastomeric rubber and bitumenised laminated boards.

Bitumenised fabric sheets - consist of a central absorbent material (fleece or fabric), which is impregnated and coated with bitumen. Core materials vary from simple rag to polyester depending on the physical properties required. BS8102 gives recommendations for the use of bituminous sheet membranes, the preferred types being BS747 Type 5B and BS743 Class A. They are highly resistant to both water and water vapour. Typical vapour transmission resistance is 3 GNs/kg per fully bonded layer.

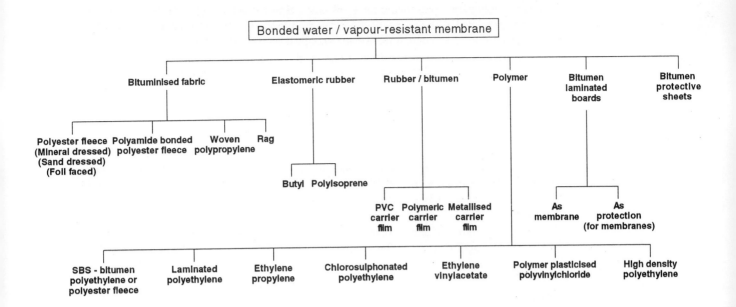

Figure 7.1 Generic types of bonded preformed sheet membrane

The flexibility and bonding of bituminous sheets is temperature-sensitive. Stiffness tends to increase with decreasing temperatures.

The tear resistance and bursting resistance of materials with polymer cores, e.g. BS747 Type 5B, is generally good. The sheets can generally be cut with a knife, but this becomes increasingly difficult at lower temperatures.

Bituminous sheets are generally not chemically resistant to hydrocarbon or chlorinated hydrocarbon solvents, which may cause loss of bitumen on long-term exposure (> 24 hours), softening and loss of waterproofing integrity. Most uncontaminated groundwaters have little effect.

Multi-layer tanking is commonly associated with the use of bituminous sheeting which has the advantage of being less dependent on high standards of workmanship and can be built up to any required thickness, to increase the puncture resistance, reliability and movement capability.

Polymeric sheet membranes - consist of extruded blends of various base polymers to which are added other polymers, binders, plasticisers and inert fillers. The resistance of the bulk material to the passage of water is high. However, as with all sheet systems, joints are the critical feature. Vapour transmission resistance is variable with composition and grade but is typically in the range 2 to 20 GNs/kg per fully bonded layer.

Polymeric sheets are generally formulated to be flexible over a wide range of temperatures, though most materials show increased stiffness at low temperatures, particularly laminated and bitumenised polyethylene. The resistance to unrolling of sheets is also temperature-related.

They are generally easier to cut than other types of membrane, owing to their temperature behaviour. Aggregate penetration resistance is also generally higher than for bitumenised fabric. Some laminated polyethylene sheets, however, have only poor penetration resistance.

Composite polymeric sheet membranes are now being formulated specifically to overcome the problems associated with the use of a bonded membrane for reverse tanking (i.e. it acts in a similar fashion to an unbonded membrane should it be damaged and water penetrate). These sheets, consisting of an HDPE carrier, a laminated synthetic adhesive, a protective elastomeric compound and a PTE (mylar) release sheet, are mechanically fixed to the support system through a selvage. The sheets are lapped to provide protection to the selvage and prevent moisture penetration. Concrete should be poured within 30 days of fixing the membrane, to prevent deterioration of elastomer and adhesive. After setting, the membrane becomes firmly bonded to the freshly placed concrete.

Elastomeric rubber sheets - usually calendered and vulcanized (chemically treated with sulphur), butyl or isoprene rubber. Some butyl rubber sheets may be laminated with saturated felt on the underside. Water transmission through these membranes is low. They are generally flexible but this is dependent on whether they are laminated with other materials. Tear resistance and aggregate penetration resistance are good. Some compositions, particularly butyl rubber, are susceptible to attack by organic solvents. Membranes with good chemical resistance are also available.

Bitumenised laminated boards - consist of layers of bitumen-saturated felt, sandwiching bitumen-saturated finely crushed aggregate. They are frequently used as protection boards for membranes but confer some additional (minor) water-resistance. Most systems require the use of bonding compounds but some self-adhesive systems are available. Their resistance to the passage of water is generally low and they have moderately high water absorption, which may result in damage if frozen.

7.3.1.3 Unbonded preformed sheet membranes

Unbonded sheets, like their bonded counterparts, take the form of either flexible sheets, usually in roll form with joints formed by welding, or boards connected by suitable overlaps. The principal division of this group of materials is into barrier and hydrophilic membranes (see Figure 7.2).

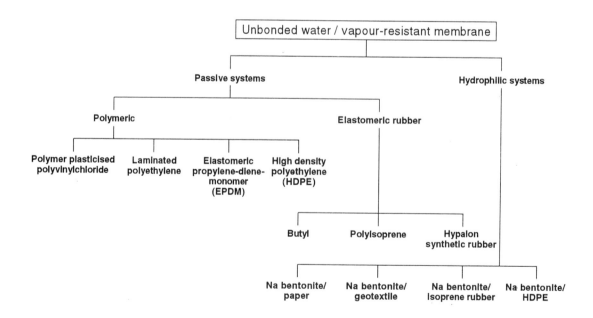

Figure 7.2 Generic types of unbonded preformed sheet membrane

(a)   Barrier

Membranes used in basement construction are generally based either on polymers or elastomeric rubber. They rely on perfect joints to a far greater extent than do bonded membranes, as water, once it has penetrated the membrane, can travel beneath it to any imperfections in the structure. It is for this reason that they are usually only used on well-drained sites. Some sheets that function primarily as drainage systems (see Section 7.6) may be classified in this section as they also provide a high degree of water penetration resistance. The properties of these unbonded materials are essentially the same as those of bonded sheets.

(b)   Hydrophilic

Hydrophilic membranes are composite materials consisting of a carrier material (often sacrificial) of geofabric, paper, high-density polyethylene (HDPE) or isoprene rubber, which are filled or impregnated with dehydrated natural sodium bentonite, which is hydrophilic.

The hydrophilic materials in these membranes react with water, which on hydration results in swelling and the production of an impermeable gel, which seals the surface to which they have been applied. They are applied as an unbonded membrane, mechanically fixed to the substrate surface, but on hydration the gel formed bonds to the surface with good adhesion. They must, however, be adequately confined by the backfill to prevent excessive swelling and loss of gel. In the hydrated state they are highly susceptible to damage if they become fully hydrated prematurely or by subsequent excavation.

The sheets are generally flexible and are nailed into place. Care should be taken with some types of sheet which contain granular sodium bentonite to ensure that it is not lost when they are cut or nailed to the substrate. Surface preparation does not need to be as rigorous for these materials as for bonded sheets; surface irregularities of up to ±10 mm can be accommodated on hydration.

Manufacturers' tests carried out on these types of material have shown them to have a high resistance to the passage of water vapour.

The rate of hydration of the hydrophilic phase is dependent on the conditions of the site, i.e. the amount of water available for hydration and the water resistance of the carrier material. Geofabrics have little resistance to water and therefore react rapidly, while HDPE has a high resistance to water and hydration will only occur initially at joints and at punctures or fixing points in the carrier, which will self-heal on hydration. Care should be taken with the fast-acting materials to ensure that hydration does not occur prior to fixing. Where long periods of site exposure are unavoidable, sheets with increased weather (water) resistance should be used. If a sheet becomes hydrated and swells prior to backfilling against walls or concreting floor slabs it should be replaced.

Chemical resistance is generally good, although the hydration of sodium bentonite may be inhibited in the presence of high concentrations of salts, particularly calcium.

When in intimate contact with the structure, owing to its self-healing properties the hydrophilic gel can accommodate subsequent cracks in the structure in excess of 0.6 mm as well as small punctures in the membrane.

Joints between panels are constructed by self-sealing overlaps. Bentonitic sealants are also available for added protection. At construction joints in walls, or in areas of contaminated ground, double layers may be necessary.

Membranes are likely to be exposed to cyclic variations of external moisture with fluctuating water level during the life of the structure. In general, soils below a certain depth will contain sufficient moisture to maintain adequate hydration of the membrane, once fully hydrated. Within the surface zone, soils experience more extreme seasonal variation in moisture content and dehydration and rehydration of the membrane may occur.

7.3.1.4 Liquid membranes

Liquid systems generally consist of one- or two-component, moisture or chemically curing systems. A wide range of materials are available (see Figure 7.3), which can be characterised into bituminous and resinous systems. They are applied by spray or brush and when hardened form a water-resistant membrane. Surface preparation and priming are particularly important for these types of material. Outgassing (of entrapped air or moisture) from the substrate can result in the formation of blowholes. Surface laitance on concrete may also cause adhesion problems if not removed prior to application of the membrane. Liquid membranes, do however, have the advantage of being able to be applied to relatively uneven surfaces. 'Blowholes' on the surface of the concrete may be difficult to coat fully. Liquid membranes can be applied to complicated details and site damage is often easy to repair. Some can be applied in several layers thus increasing their effectiveness and crack-bridging properties.

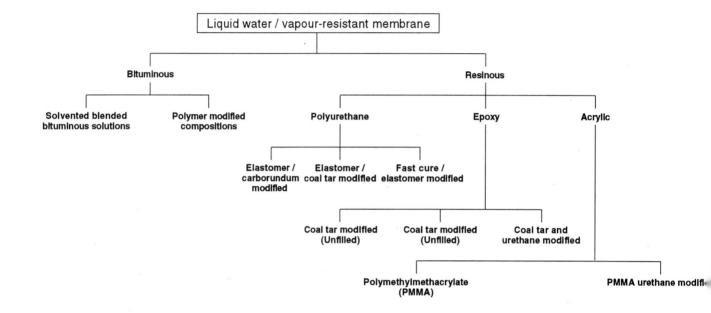

Figure 7.3 Generic types of liquid membrane system

Liquid membrane systems include:

Bituminous blended solutions dry to form a layer of bitumen. They become stiffer, less compliant and harder at low temperatures, when aggregate penetration damage may be more severe. Polymer compositions have better flexibility.

Polyurethane systems are generally thin coatings, less than 2 mm thick with good flexibility. Intercoat adhesion is poor; hence they are generally applied in a single layer. Water absorption may increase susceptibility to frost damage and be a problem with some coal-tar modified polyurethanes (this will depend on the formulation).

Epoxy resin systems have low flexibility, particularly coal-tar modified systems, which are susceptible to embrittlement at low temperatures. Some formulations are prone to pinholes which, if not treated, markedly reduce water resistance and local adhesion. They are highly resistant to chemicals.

Acrylic resin systems remain flexible over a wide temperature range. They are resistant to site damage, have good bond and high water resistance.

7.3.1.5 Water-resistant cementitious renders and polymer/cement coatings

BS8102 gives recommendations for the use of internally applied cementitious render and polymer/cement-based coatings. Water-resistant render systems have been used for 80 years in the UK for this purpose, and proprietary systems are available from several manufacturers, which are sold for both internal and external use. Mixes are designed so that a discontinuous network of pores and capillaries is formed within the multi-layer composition of the render system. The cementitious render consists of blended mixes of cement and fine aggregates with admixtures, which further block pores within the cement paste matrix or increase its density, thereby increasing its resistance to the passage of water. The admixtures used to achieve this effect are silicates of the soda glass type.

The more recently introduced water-resistant polymer/cement-based coatings are based on blends of cement and fine fillers (including fine sand) with or without microsilica with a pre-batched quantity of SBR or an acrylic-based copolymer. The former reacts with lime from the hydrating cement to form calcium and sodium silicate hydrates; the latter dries to forms a three-dimensional latex network through the paste.

Surface preparation is important in all cases to ensure a good bond to the substrate. BS8102 recommends bush-hammering smooth concrete and masonry surfaces to obtain a good mechanical key. Care should be taken to ensure that this does not damage the aggregate at the surface of the concrete or result in subsurface microcracking in masonry, thereby reducing bond. Grit blasting and water jetting are suitable preparation techniques in order to achieve a defect-free finish. Some systems require the use of substrate primers.

All water-resistant cementitious systems should be applied by suitably experienced contracting organisations in accordance with the manufacturer's instructions or specification. Many contracting organisations will provide guarantees for this type of work.

Water-resistant cementitious systems generally have a high resistance to water penetration but do allow the passage of water vapour. Their resistance to chemicals in soil and groundwater should be regarded as the same as that of concrete having a similar cement content, cement type and water/cementitious ratio.

7.3.2 Internal barrier materials

The principal technical problem with the use of barrier materials on the inside of a structure is the need to contain the hydrostatic pressure, which tends to push the membrane off the substrate. A substantial loading coat must therefore be used that is sufficient to withstand this pressure either by gravity, or tied back to the basement structure. The structural consequences of this are significant. The bond strength of the membrane is also required to be in excess of the maximum hydrostatic pressure and requires an adhesive system not subject to long-term creep or flow. Internal barrier systems are useful for upgrading existing basements (see Chapter 5) but should not be used as the primary barrier in new designs.

Internal barrier systems include:

7.3.2.1 Mastic asphalt

Comments in 7.3.1.1 regarding its external use apply equally. In addition it should be noted that on floors, blowholes frequently form in the first layer. This may be eliminated by the use of a paper, or glassfibre tissue insulating layer. There is, however, a consequential loss of bond to the substrate, and a substantial loading coat becomes essential.

7.3.2.2 Bonded preformed sheet membranes

Particular care should be taken when installing synthetic rubber/elastomer or polymer sheet membranes on the internal face of a wall to ensure that it is sufficiently dry for bonding to be effective and that the loading coat is sufficient to prevent external hydrostatic pressure building up behind the sheet, causing it to blister and debond.

Bitumenised laminated boards may also be required as protection to other types of membrane. If the membrane is punctured, the protection board may provide a moisture path around the structure.

7.3.2.3 Unbonded preformed sheet membranes

Unbonded sheets may be used internally provided the joints are made reliably watertight and a sufficiently thick loading coat is provided.

7.3.2.4 Liquid membranes

Both vapour-permeable and impermeable liquid systems are available. Vapour-impermeable systems will debond from the substrate if the vapour pressure exceeds the bond strength. Chemical curing systems (including organic solvent-based primers) may, during application and curing, give off fumes, which are a hazard (toxic and flammable) in confined spaces unless they are adequately ventilated[7.8].

7.3.2.5 Water-resistant cementitious renders and polymer/cement coatings

As Section 7.3.1.5, for external tanking systems.

7.4 WATERSTOPS

Construction and movement joints in concrete structures are vulnerable points for water ingress, and extra protection may be provided. Two types of joint in concrete basement construction are:

1. continuously reinforced construction joints, where only slight opening due to shrinkage is likely
2. joints designed to accommodate movement.

When a concrete structure is intended to be water-resistant (Type B protection), all construction joints likely to open can be given additional protection by the use of a waterstop (materials crossing joints to provide a barrier, or longer water path, to the transmission of water). Waterstops are designed for either construction or movement joints, and the properties of the products differ accordingly. Each type is also influenced by the location in which it is used:

1. external waterstops: cast into, or applied to the external surface of the concrete
2. internal waterstops: cast into the body of the concrete.

Incorrectly fitted waterstops have been known to reduce rather than improve the moisture resistance of a concrete structure (see Section 3.7). Consequently there are differences of opinion as to whether waterstops should be used and which types are more effective in particular cases.

BS8007: 1987 states in Section 5.4 *'it is not necessary to incorporate waterstops in properly constructed construction joints'*. Yet BS8102: 1990 states, in Section 14, *'in some circumstances the use of waterstops is considered desirable'*, and in Section 6.2 of BS8102: 1990 for Type B protection *'waterstops should be used in all construction joints'* for Grade 1 basements designed in accordance with BS8110: Part 2: 1985 with calculated flexural and thermal crack widths not exceeding 0.3 mm. The use of waterstops is fully reviewed in CIRIA publication FR/CP/17[7.9].

Against a background of conflicting code requirements it is reasonable to conclude that, if a designer has taken full cognisance of the permeability of the ground and expected water levels, and all reasonable precautions to control random cracking and the opening of joints, and is satisfied that method or performance specifications and site supervision are appropriate to fulfil his intentions, he may reasonably omit waterstops, joggles and kickers in appropriate circumstances.

Although movement joints are less likely to be required in basements than in above-ground structures, where they occur, it is essential to provide a waterstop.

7.4.1 External waterstops

Most modern waterstops are manufactured from PVC, though where greater movement capability is required rubber may be used. They consist of flexible strips with a complicated cross section to key into the concrete that is cast against them. They work on the valve and tortuous path principle: i.e. the water path around the edge of the barrier is lengthened and blocked by the many projections, and the lateral forces that act on the projections seal the water path.

Where waterstops are considered necessary, a fully continuous system should be installed at all joints (excepting settlement joints where longitudinal shear may pull the waterstop out of the wall) including kickers, where a wide strip (at least 300 mm) should be used to protect possibly lesser-quality concrete. Care must be taken during installation to position the waterstop accurately in the joint and to ensure that it does not become displaced during concreting. Fixing, by nailing to the shuttering or blinding, should make use of the external flange included on most modern designs for this purpose. Shutters should be struck carefully to ensure that the fixed waterstop is not pulled free. Some designs have an end key on the flange to minimise the risk of pull-out.

Difficulties in making the waterstops follow the shape of the concrete sometimes arise, especially when the base slab has a toe protruding in front of the wall face where the waterstop has to follow a complicated path. Consultation with the manufacturer is strongly recommended during the design of the structure. Specially fabricated details such as corners are readily available, and these should be used in preference to joints manufactured on site, which should be restricted to simple butt joints between similar materials. If a badly made joint in a waterstop (or free end) is exposed to hydrostatic pressure, water will enter and may follow a path along the waterstop and emerge at a position remote from the entry point, where another imperfection, in either the waterstop or concrete, is situated. Once a waterstop has been cast into a wall it is not possible to adjust its position. Hence any movement of the waterstop during placing of the concrete will result in its not functioning correctly and may require remedial work to the wall to prevent water penetration (see Section 5.2).

7.4.2 Waterstops internal to the in-situ wall and base slab

Internal waterstops may be further subdivided into:

- barrier systems
- hydrophilic systems
- co-extruded systems
- post-grouted tubes.

7.4.2.1 Barrier systems

These are manufactured from PVC, rubber or metal and work on the same principles as external waterstops. They are modified for use in construction or expansion joints in a similar fashion to external waterstops. In general, all the requirements for the use of external waterstops need to be applied to internal waterstops; in particular, fixing is of primary importance as they are susceptible to folding over as concrete is placed above them. Sufficient space should also be allowed between the waterstops and any adjacent reinforcement to ensure that the concrete can be properly compacted around both.

Internal waterstops placed horizontally within a base slab should generally be avoided owing to the difficulties of compacting concrete around it, along its full length. Where it is necessary to make a transition to the internal form of waterstop for wall construction, premoulded junction pieces are available.

Metal waterstops are now rarely used, although they are less likely to be distorted, disturbed in casting or damaged during stop end removal and scabbling of the concrete at the joint face. They are less flexible for installation and in accommodating changes of profile and may be susceptible to corrosion.

Rubber waterstops are used primarily where ground movements are anticipated. Difficulties in jointing and forming junctions on site may be experienced as the material has to be hot-vulcanised to form an effective joint. Equipment and methods are, however, available to make reliable and effective site joints. 'Low modulus' PVC waterstops offer comparable performance, but with simplified fabrication and assembly. However, where cyclic or large magnitude movements are expected rubber waterstops are still preferred.

PVC waterstops are the most commonly employed product in modern structures. They can be factory formed into complex shapes more easily than rubber waterstops and can be more easily jointed at site.

7.4.2.2 Hydrophilic systems

Hydrophilic materials, as with the sheet membranes, consist of an inert carrier material (consisting of butyl, chloroprene rubber, etc.) which has been impregnated with either a hydrophilic resin or natural sodium bentonite. Both react with water causing the waterstop to swell and effectively seal the joint, provided the joint width does not exceed the swelling capacity of the material. They must remain moist to retain their water resistance.

The swelling ability and particularly the reversibility may be adversely affected by the environment, particularly high and low pH and high salt concentrations.

These materials come in strip form and should be fixed as centrally as possible at the joint. If the strips are displaced toward the edge of the concrete the high swell pressures generated may result in cracking and spalling of the joint edges. They can be laid in chases, nailed to a flat joint surface or fixed in expanded metal cages attached to the concrete surfaces. Some systems are self-adhesive. When hydrated they can withstand high hydrostatic pressures (up to 70 m) when adequately confined.

The strips should be installed immediately prior to placing the concrete to prevent premature expansion. If this occurs the material should be removed and replaced. As the swell time response is relatively slow, these materials are not effective in movement joints.

7.4.2.3 Co-extruded systems

These are similar to passive waterstops but the bulb-ends are co-extruded with hydrophilic materials designed to perform as described above, thus providing a degree of additional contact pressure at the bulb ends if water reaches that point.

Jointing is carried out in a similar fashion to that for passive systems, except that the hydrophilic materials are simply butted together. Their expansion seals any gap when they become wetted.

7.4.2.4 Post-grouted tubes

Injection hose systems consist of a perforated or semi-permeable tube which is fixed at the concrete joint surface. There are a number of fixing methods e.g. by clips, brackets or mesh. The tube is designed to remain open under the pressure of the next pour of concrete. The ends of the tube are either attached to special shutter connectors or allowed to protrude under the shutter. After the concrete has been placed and allowed to harden and cure, resin or cementitious grout is injected into the tube. Some systems allow the tube to be flushed out, after use, and thus remain open for reinjection, should it prove necessary. Resin may also be injected by post-drill and grout techniques, in the case of remedial works (see Chapter 5).

A number of different injection resins can be used, depending on the width of the joint and the expected degree of movement e.g. low viscosity polyurethane, for hairline cracks with a limited amount of expected movement.

The injection hose can be used between new concrete and existing structures, such as in the case of a basement extension.

7.5   JOINT FILLERS AND SEALANTS

7.5.1   Joint fillers

Joint fillers are used to support sealants in association with waterstops in movement joints in reinforced concrete construction. They are usually supplied as preformed sheets which are cut to size on site. Generic groups include:

- fibre board (wood fibres impregnated with bitumen).
- cork
- closed-cell polyethylene
- closed-cell rubber.

Care is required when specifying a filler board to eliminate material incompatibility: for example, some elastomeric sealants are not compatible with bitumen. Bitumen boards when raked out to allow the sealant to be placed may contaminate the substrate surface, resulting in sealant failure.

7.5.2   Joint sealants

Joint sealants can be used in association with suitable joint fillers in movement joints or placed in preformed slots in daywork joints. They may be applied by trowel, by gun or by pouring into the slot. The behaviour of sealants after placing and curing ranges from almost fully plastic to almost fully elastic. Generic groups for use in basement construction include:

- elastomeric two-part polysulphide, gun-applied or poured cold
- elastomeric two-part polyurethane, gun-applied or poured cold
- elastomeric one-part polyurethane, gun-applied or poured cold
- thermoplastic rubber bitumen, poured hot (horizontal joints)
- rubber bitumen, poured cold (vertical joints).

Elastomeric materials will accommodate early movement as they experience an acceptable level of cure within a relatively short time period. They are used in association with bond breakers. Examples of the movement accommodation factors and rates of cure for different generic groups of sealants are set out in Table 7.1.

Table 7.1   Relationship between rate of cure and movement accommodation factor for generic groups of sealants

Sealant type	Rate of cure*	Movement accommodation
Thermoplastic	Very fast	Low/medium
Elastomeric (two-part)	Fast	High
Elastomeric (one-part)	Slow	High
Rubber bitumen, poured cold	Slow	Medium

*   The faster the rate of cure of the sealant, the better it will be at accommodating early movement.

Further details on joint sealants can be found in CIRIA publications TN128 (1987)[7.10], SP80 (1991)[7.11] and R128 (1992)[7.12].

7.5.3   Preformed strip sealants

The use of a preformed strip sealant with an unbonded section over the joint can often provide a more reliable method of sealing a joint than the use of a sealant material. The sealant should not, however, be used as the primary system of water exclusion at movement joints. Generic groups include:

- bitumen rubber
- hypalon - overlay strip
- neoprene - insertion strip
- chlorinated polyethylene
- EPDM - insertion or overlay strip
- butyl and butyl laminate - overlay strip.

Care should be taken when specifying a strip sealant to ensure compatibility with any membrane system. Adhesion at the edge of strips may be prone to failure in conditions of continuous immersion. They are generally not used internally where their adhesion would have to withstand hydrostatic pressure.

7.6   EXTERNAL DRAINAGE SYSTEMS

External drainage systems can be used in some cases to prevent local build-up of hydrostatic pressure against the walls of the structure. This is unlikely to be feasible where diaphragm or piled wall construction is used (see Chapter 4), or where there are restrictions on external excavation. The traditional method of producing an external drainage zone using a porous pipe, at the base of a free-draining aggregate layer separated from the subsoil by a geofabric filter membrane, is described in BS8102. Despite carrying out additional excavation around the site, the laying of a geofabric and the replacement of the existing subsoil with clean aggregate, drainage systems still have a risk of blockage, which should be considered at the design stage. An external drainage system can never be better than its ultimate discharge point. The risk of general flooding around the structure should also be assessed.

Sheet drainage systems consisting of a polypropylene or polyester geofabric filter and a low permeability high-density polyethylene (HDPE) profiled sheet are being used to replace the more traditional methods. They are fixed with battens shot-fired to the substrate using masonry nails (this method may, however, lead to problems by providing water paths into the substrate), with dowel pins into holes, with adhesive-backed pins bonded to the substrate pushed through the sheet (this however, punctures the sheet), or with self-adhesive tape. The last option is preferred (as this does not damage the integrity of the sheet). Joints are produced by laps (maximum 200 mm) of the profiled sheets and geofabric. The leading edge of the sheets should be covered with a preformed profile to prevent debris from clogging the fabric and the air void.

The profiled sheet forms an impervious barrier with a continuous air space (which prevents moisture bridging and improves thermal insulation), providing a free drainage cavity to remove groundwater. The sheets can be laid either to an existing land drain (surrounded by aggregate) or to perforated clay pipes or fin drains (polypropylene core surrounded by geofabric) with the geofabric wrapped around them to prevent blockage.

Several designs of sheet are available, primarily defined on the depth and diameter of the 'studs' in the HDPE backing sheet. Selection should depend on the expected hydrostatic pressure and avoidance of the possibility of long-term build-up of silt in the cavity.

7.7   INTERNAL DRAINAGE SYSTEMS

Profiled HDPE sheets (similar to those described above but without the geofabric) are now being used to upgrade the internal environment and to improve some of the traditional forms of drained cavity wall construction (see also Sections 3.8 and 5.3). The sheets typically manufactured from high-density polyethylene can be fixed to the external wall or floor slab of the basement where they form a drainage void, used to collect infiltrating water and route it to drainage channels or sumps.

The sheets are fixed to the substrate by the manufacturer's recommended method at approximately 500 mm centres. Fixing nails should be fitted with a flexible plastic washer to prevent damage to the sheet and provide an additional seal. The sheets are sufficiently flexible to be turned around 90° and three-way corners, e.g. from vertical walls to the floor slab, but are sufficiently strong to support the load of wet concrete cast against them. End and side laps should be a minimum 200 mm wide and the edges of the sheets should be sealed with self-adhesive rubberised bitumen tape. Where services must pass through the drained cavity, additional protection should be provided by the use of a bonded sheet membrane to seal around the pipes.

There are a range of grades of sheets available based on 'stud' height which should be selected for different drainage requirements: i.e. the higher the stud the greater the drainage capacity and avoidance of the possibility of long-term build-up of silt in the cavity. The sheets must be installed the correct way up; some are not reversible, and the moisture resistance will be dependent on the quality of the joints.

The internal wall or floor screed (where these sheets form a cavity beneath floor slabs) can be cast or built (in the case of masonry internal walls) directly against the sheet, thus increasing available floor space; i.e. the wall/floor cavity may be reduced from 75 mm as recommended in BS8102 to the depth of the sheet. The requirements for ventilation will depend on the type of sheet selected, the method and type of fixing and the required internal environment.

7.8   PROTECTION BOARDS

Most tanking systems are susceptible to impact damage after installation either from other trades or from sharp objects during backfilling. They therefore require protection to preserve their integrity. Hydrophilic membranes do not normally require protection boards as they can impede water contact and interfere with the hydration process.

There are a number of types of stiff board with good mechanical properties manufactured for this purpose. Such boards are usually based on bitumen with aggregates or fibres included to improve the mechanical properties. They may also provide some additional resistance to water ingress if the joints are sealed with adhesive and taped over. Generic groups include:

- modified bitumen with cork aggregate
- modified bitumen with mineral aggregate
- modified bitumen with natural fibres
- non-bituminous boards.

Boards should be used to protect the membrane immediately after its installation wherever there is the likelihood of site damage, e.g. from backfilling operations or reinforcement fixing, or as protection to horizontal membranes beneath load-bearing foundations.

REFERENCES

7.1   HARRISON, T.A.
        Early-age thermal crack control in concrete
        CIRIA Report 91, 1993

7.2   CONCRETE SOCIETY
        Non-structural cracks in concrete
        Concrete Society Technical Report, CSTR No. 22, 1982

7.3   FÉDÉRATION INTERNATIONAL DE LA PRÉCONTRAINTE
        Condensed silica fume in concrete
        FIP state of the art report, Thomas Telford Ltd, 1988

7.4   RAMACHANDRAN, V.S.
        Concrete admixtures handbook: properties, science and technology
        Noyes Publishers, USA, 1984

7.5   BRICK DEVELOPMENT ASSOCIATION
        Brickwork durability
        BDA Design Note 7, 1986

7.6   JOHNSON, R.A., LEEK, D.S. and KING, E.S
        Waterproofing and repairing underground reservoir roofs
        CIRIA Technical Note 145, 1991

7.7   MASTIC ASPHALT COUNCIL & EMPLOYERS FEDERATION/MASTIC
        ASPHALT PRODUCERS ASSOCIATION
        Tanking handbook
        MACEF, 1990

7.8   CONSTRUCTION INDUSTRY RESEARCH AND INFORMATION ASSOCIATION
        A guide to the control of substances hazardous to health in design and construction
        CIRIA, Report 125, 1993

7.9   CONSTRUCTION INDUSTRY RESEARCH AND INFORMATION ASSOCIATION
        The design and construction of joints in concrete structures
        CIRIA, Report FR/CP/17, 1994

7.10   CONSTRUCTION INDUSTRY RESEARCH AND INFORMATION ASSOCIATION
        Civil engineering sealants in wet conditions - review of performance and interim guidance on use
        CIRIA, Technical Note 128, 1987

7.11   CONSTRUCTION INDUSTRY RESEARCH AND INFORMATION ASSOCIATION
        Manual of good practice in sealant application
        CIRIA/BASA, Special Publication 80, 1991

7.12   CONSTRUCTION INDUSTRY RESEARCH AND INFORMATION ASSOCIATION
        Performance of sealants in wet conditions - joint surfaces
        CIRIA, Report 128, 1992

8   Ancillary considerations

8.1   PRE-DESIGN CONSIDERATIONS

■. The archaeology underlying the site must be considered and advice on its protection obtained: e.g. from the Corporation of London, local plan policies (January 1989). Programme and cost implications must also be taken into account.

■ The effect of the new building on surrounding buildings and services must be considered and damage assessments, condition surveys, etc., must be carried out.

8.2   PIPES AND OTHER SERVICES

■ If the principle of a continuous water-resistant barrier is accepted (Type A protection), then clearly precautions must be taken where services pass through the envelope or where fixings penetrate the barrier (see Figure 8.1).

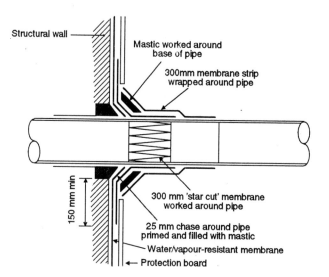

Figure 8.1 Pipe penetration through water/vapour-resistant membrane

■ In the case of metallic and plastic pipework (or more usually sleeves around pipes) subjected to hydrostatic pressure, a caulking groove may be formed around the pipe on the inside face of the box. The groove is sealed, normally with a bitumastic sealant, internal render, if used, may be butted up to the pipe.

■ Non-metallic pipes (and, in particular, salt-glazed earthenware) may have their surfaces specially prepared before casting into the concrete. Provided a sufficient length of prepared pipe projects beyond the concrete face it may be possible to bond an internal render direct to the surface.

■ the building services engineer must make known to the structural engineer any provisions affecting the structure, at an early stage in the design. Likewise, the structural engineer must advise on the risk of any differential settlement occurring which may affect services passing through or outside the structure.

■ Every effort must be made by the design team to pre-plan all service entries. Duct openings that have to be provided at the last moment because of lack of planning frequently present a leakage risk. Additional reinforcement may be required, particularly at corners of openings' to counteract the concentration of shrinkage stresses at such positions.

■ Services that pass through the wall at high level and are grouped together in one or two large openings isolate the potential problems of leakage. When this is not possible, and individual pipes are required to pass through the wall, a number of points of weakness may be formed in the passive protection. Good-quality concrete, well compacted around pipes, may provide sufficient water-resistance, but puddle flanges may be used on individual pipes at this point. However, there is some difference of opinion on this subject, as a badly placed flange can form a channel for moisture ingress. The final decision must be the responsibility of the designer. Particular care must be given to the detailed design at these points to ensure that congestion of reinforcement is avoided so that concrete can be easily poured and compacted around the pipe.

■ Wherever piped services run from an external duct or loosely filled surface excavation into the basement, surface water can collect at this point. The simple precaution of providing a puddle clay dam (or half brick wall) at the junction between the duct and wall may be an effective countermeasure. This is one of the points of particular sensitivity for ingress of water into the basement.

■ Sufficient access to all services, including pipes, cables, and mechanical and electrical plant, will probably be required both during construction and subsequently for maintenance.

■ Problems with services passing under a basement may occur due to water ingress into ducting, which can be particularly hazardous for electric cables, as access for maintenance is difficult.

8.3 FIXINGS IN WATER-RESISTANT CEMENTITIOUS RENDER

■ Where the position and size of fixings are known, pockets may be cast into the concrete box, sized to suit the fixing and the thickness of render, and also to provide sufficient grouting or working space. The pocket may also be lined with the water-resistant render and the fixing grouted in. The smallest size of pocket, for a single bolt fixing, is 150 mm square by 100 mm deep (see Figure 8.2).

■ Domestic cable support brackets, if they are light, may be attached to timber battens bonded to the rendered surface (see Figure 8.3).

8.4 LIGHTNING CONDUCTORS

■ The requirement for lightning conductors should be considered prior to the design of the passive protection. Rods driven through the base slab are unlikely to be acceptable. An example of an earth electrode seal for use within a tanked structure is given in Figure 24 of BS6651: 1990.

8.5 INTERNAL DRAINAGE

■ External ramp access to a basement may require a cut-off channel, at the top and/or foot, connected to a drain or sump.

■ For car parks, plant rooms, etc., the floor should be provided with adequate falls for drainage. Particular attention is required to avoid ponding at the foot of ramps and staircases.

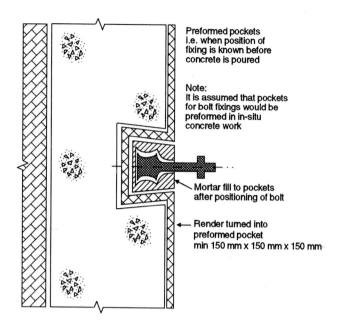

Preformed pockets
i.e. when position of
fixing is known before
concrete is poured

Note:
It is assumed that pockets
for bolt fixings would be
preformed in in-situ
concrete work

Mortar fill to pockets
after positioning of bolt

Render turned into
preformed pocket
min 150 mm x 150 mm x 150 mm

Figure 8.2 Example of fixing in a preformed pocket in
association with a water-resistant
cementitious render

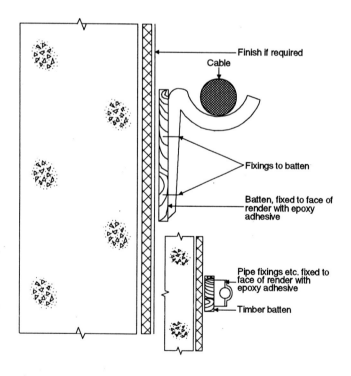

Finish if required

Cable

Fixings to batten

Batten, fixed to face of
render with epoxy
adhesive

Pipe fixings etc. fixed to
face of render with
epoxy adhesive

Timber batten

Figure 8.3 Example of light cable support brackets
bonded to water-resistant cementitious
render

- Where a drained cavity is included in the construction, access doors provided in the inner wall at regular intervals for inspection and cleaning of the cavity may be advantageous. Where possible, such doors should coincide with downpipes.

- A factor of safety in sump sizes and duplicate pumps in a basement should be considered by the designer. The surplus capacity will be available in the event of a pump breakdown, removal for maintenance or for additional drainage should higher than expected basement leakage occur.

- Automatic pump switches in sumps may malfunction and regular inspection, testing and maintenance are essential to ensure that they work satisfactorily. Multiple switches should be considered by the designer.

8.6 VOID FORMERS

- Void formers, provided below some basement floors to counter the effects of ground heave, should be prevented from expanding until required. This may be achieved by wrapping them in polythene, with the water introduced in a controlled manner through a pipe.

- Care should be taken with the use of compressible filler boards (of the clay/paper type) below basement constructions, which in certain ground environments can rapidly generate large quantities of methane. This may migrate into poorly ventilated basements and build up to reach the lower explosive limit.

8.7 DETAILING OF STAIRS

- The stairs or lower flights serving a basement may be specified as removable in order to facilitate repairs and continuity of waterproofing in the basement structure.

9 Procedures: QA, contracts, maintenance

9.1 INTRODUCTION

Most basement problems are probably caused by incorrect design, incorrect materials selection and/or use, poor workmanship or lack of maintenance. The incorporation of formal quality systems into the management of construction and repair activities provides a framework for effective, demonstrable, project management. When used throughout the project, from inception to implementation and monitoring, project planning is aided and coordination between the project stages defined. In addition, the project structure and the responsibilities of the project participants are determined and coordinated, thus reducing the likelihood of omission or overlap.

A further major advantage of the use of formal quality systems is that documentation is generated systematically throughout the project. If correctly structured, the documentation will demonstrate that requirements have been defined and that work has been implemented that meets these requirements.

Furthermore, the system for subsequent monitoring of performance is developed and documented in conjunction with the design. Provided that the integrity of the personnel carrying out the monitoring is accepted by all parties, the results of the monitoring exercise provide a documented basis for assessment of continuing performance acceptability.

Although, in theory, QA could be incorporated into selected sections of the development and implementation process, this is not likely to be satisfactory. The interrelation of each section with others and the need to coordinate between sections makes selective implementation of QA difficult. Indeed, one of the products of QA is to ensure that the interaction of all parties is considered and suitable arrangements made.

The implementation and continuing effectiveness of the quality system are monitored through quality audits. These investigate the quality system and do not question the technical adequacy of the work. The competence of the personnel carrying out the work is not, therefore, compromised.

Quality audits may, and almost certainly will be carried out internally (first-party audits). In addition, in order to give confidence to other parties, audits may be carried out by the client (second-party audits), or by an organisation independent of the contract (third-party audits). The scope and extent of the audit programme will vary according to the sensitivity of the project, company practice and the need to verify compliance. The type of audit chosen (i.e. first-, second- or third- party) will be dependent on the availability of resources to carry out the audit and on the degree of independence required of the audit team.

In some industrial sectors (particularly in manufacturing and materials supply), schemes have been developed whereby contractors/suppliers gain certification for their in-house systems. This has the advantages of minimising duplication of auditing effort and providing immediate recognition that a quality system has been developed and implemented. It is, however, necessary to confirm that the certification applies to the particular material, product, process or activity under consideration.

The question of guarantees, responsibilities and insurance is controversial. Limited, short-term, insurance-backed guarantees (i.e. up to 15 years) are available in some cases. Insurance-backed guarantees possibly involve additional design evaluation and site supervision checks and may in future extend to longer-term performance contracts.

Where the intention is to obtain such guarantees, the underwriters should be involved as early as possible in the design process. However, structural liability does not ensure that the works will comply with the requirements, only that some of the costs may be recoverable in the event of non-compliance.

9.2   DURING THE DESIGN OR ASSESSMENT PROCEDURE

The development of objective criteria of success in the design, or repair of basements requires care, and the assurance of quality in either is principally achieved at two stages:-

1.   the definition of the performance requirements and their specification

2.   the preparation of method statements on workmanship and how performance testing is to be carried out.

Review and approval of the results of these two stages is an essential feature of the quality system, with key features particular to each stage of the process. In particular the performance, requirements should be included in the quality plan (see Figure 3.1).

There are a number of aspects of importance in assuring quality in basements that are particular to each stage.

9.2.1   Assessment of existing basements

The key elements are:

■   qualification and experience of staff
■   thorough evaluation of the cause(s) of the condition - not simply the major cause
■   collection of relevant data
■   prognosis for future life span - with and without remedial treatment.

The last provides the starting point for any remedial works.

9.2.2   Design of new basements

The key elements are:

■   preparation of the design intent and review against the client's brief
■   coordination of the summary of the design predictions, the construction specification and the original performance specification including the internal and external environmental conditions. The construction specification should contain provisions for any necessary remedial works to defects and subsequent compliance.

The above activities should be identified in the design phase as key reviews and subject to formal review, corrective action as appropriate and final approval. The specification must lay down clear objective criteria, not just 'to the Engineer's satisfaction'.

9.2.3   Construction/remedial works

The key elements are:

■   preparation and review of method statements
■   verification of the experience of operatives for particular activities
■   testing and verification of material properties
■   supervision of activities
■   full records of the measurement of parameters required to meet objective criteria (including provision for their long-term storage and retrieval).

In the last activity approval should not be given against an activity such as:

'waterstop in place? - yes/no'

but to a quantified statement:

'Maximum deviation from line '+x', '-y': within tolerance ? - yes.

Method statements must pay particular attention to matters such as surface preparation, jointing, material properties, prior to placing and curing. These are the essence of water and vapour protection in construction.

9.3   DURING MATERIALS SELECTION AND TESTING

Quality assurance for materials selection and testing should provide documentation confirming compliance with the specification with regard to:

- handling, storage, packaging and delivery
- materials control and traceability
- testing procedures and dates
- calibration of testing equipment
- field testing of environmental control system.

A requirement for documentation to substantiate the conformance of materials to specification can be included in the supply contract. It could also be stipulated that the supplier operate within a formal quality system, thus providing confidence of conformance to specification.

Such a system would include documented materials control and traceability procedures. It would also identify the inspection and test regime and the procedures to be followed in the event that a non-conforming material were identified.

The adequacy of the quality system could be substantiated through independent quality audits (a requirement for access to carry out audits should be included in the contract documentation) or through reliance on third party certification by a recognised body.

As most materials are susceptible to damage, the quality assurance system would include procedures for the handling, storage, packaging and delivery of the material to the site and its storage until required at the site. Where relevant material performance data are not available, a suitable testing regime must be devised.

Materials testing would also be required at various stages in the process of identification, specification and implementation of any repair programme. These stages would require definition in terms of specific testing requirements and the records of tests carried out. The materials suppliers system should also encompass the verification that testing equipment is suitably calibrated.

9.4   DURING SERVICE LIFE OF THE BASEMENT

Quality management procedures should be implemented by the building operator to ensure performance of the environmental control system. Documentation should be provided to show compliance with agreed maintenance schedules produced for the active precautions.

The key elements include:

- verification of the experience of operatives for particular activities
- testing procedures and dates
- calibration of testing equipment
- supervision of activities
- full records, of the works carried out and their maintenance (including long-term storage requirements).

10 Recent studies and further research needs

Much interest in encouraging and improving the quality of basement construction has been displayed during the preparation of this report. This has been shown by clients, designers, contractors, and construction industry associations who have revealed their experiences. Litigation relating to leaking basements has required that some of the information has had to remain confidential. This shows the benefit of having an ongoing 'clearing house' for feedback on both the problems and successes in this form of construction. It is suggested that CIRIA should be a continuing forum for this work.

There is a need to amend BS8007 and BS8110 to refer to BS8102 (the reverse cross-reference exists), to confirm the suitability (or otherwise) of BS8007 and BS8110 to basement design and construction for any particular application. This should result in more low-permeability and durable basement structures.

The design, detailing, specification and 'buildability' aspects of reinforced concrete (to both BS8007 and BS8110) as applied to basement construction need to be clarified, particularly with regard to the calculation of flexural steel and minimum quantities of reinforcement, crack spacing and crack widths in relation to early thermal and shrinkage precautions. This should result in economic basement structures which provide a degree of water resistance appropriate to the environmental control system of which they are a component part.

Parts of the Building Regulations 1990 should also be revised to see if it can be stated more clearly that the use of active precautions (heating and ventilation, etc.) can be relied upon to achieve a satisfactory internal environment, without the need for absolute vapour exclusion.

A simplified guide should be developed (possibly in the form of tables) to the relationship between wall thickness, the water resistance of the form of construction and the external hydrostatic pressure.

Successful basement construction depends, to a large extent, on workmanship standards. There is therefore a need for advisory booklets and training aids to focus on basement construction. These should be produced for building operatives less familiar with reinforced concrete construction or tanking, which are more often associated with civil engineering construction. This is necessary in the construction of basements for houses.

Part 1 of a BCA publication[10.1] reported on a cost study for partially and fully submerged shallow basements. It compared costs of using in-situ concrete construction with reinforced masonry, as well as the costs of different waterproofing methods for alternative house types (detached, semi-detached and terraced). Additional costs were suggested for the development of waterlogged sites.

Similar research could be carried out to confirm the circumstances where affordable reinforced concrete basements can be constructed by house builders, with suitably skilled tradesmen.

Part 2 of the BCA publication[10.1] gave preliminary design information for the main concrete options for basement walls with the intention of identifying where further work was required, in order to develop basements successfully in the UK.

The standards relating to basements are fragmented. This report brings together the pertinent information. This report provides for, and may be a stage in compiling, a comprehensive UK Basement Design Code of Practice or a future European Standard.

REFERENCES

10.1   BRITISH CEMENT ASSOCIATION
        Options for quality in housing
                Basements 1: Benefits, viability and costs
                Basements 2: A preliminary assessment of the design of basement walls
        BCA, 1991

Appendix A   Implications of rising groundwater

A1   INTRODUCTION

The designer of new basements should consider all the likely changes that may occur in the external environment, including the possibility of rising groundwater levels, during the life of the basement, when selecting elements that will make up the environmental control system (Section 2.3). Many older structures have been affected by rising groundwater levels. The investigation of the current condition of an existing basement (Section 5.1) should establish whether the external environment was that expected during the design or early life of the structure.

CIRIA Special Publication 69[A.1] examines the effects of the rise in level of the groundwater in the deep aquifer beneath London and sets out the critical geographical areas affected. Similar information has been published for Birmingham[A.2].

Two centuries of water extraction by pumping for domestic and industrial use had lowered the groundwater level by as much as 70 m. Changed extraction practices have led to much less water being drawn from the ground with the result that in some areas the ground water level is rising by as much as 1 m/year. If the rise continues the water pressures will cause damage to some large buildings (as well as tunnels) and increase the risk of leakage into basements.

While CIRIA SP69 explained that these serious problems could, most economically, be prevented by controlling groundwater levels by pumping, currently there is not an effective control policy, or an organisation charged with the responsibility for developing or implementing one. Therefore, for the design of new basements in areas likely to be affected, it would be prudent to assume that water levels will continue to rise. Existing buildings may require monitoring. Remedial or preventive works will be possible in some cases.

The potential effects on buildings given in CIRIA SP69 are summarised as follows:

- reduced ground bearing capacity
- uplift on foundations and slabs
- ground swelling and heave
- increased retaining wall loadings
- leakage into basements and ducts
- solution of minerals causing increased potential for chemical attack
- confinement of hazardous gases
- increased drainage requirements
- the effect of the above on temporary works including instability of excavations.

The consequences for new and existing basements are set out in Sections A2 and A3 below.

A2   CONSIDERATIONS FOR NEW BASEMENTS

The implications for design, construction and maintenance of new basements are as follows.

A2.1   Design considerations

- The best water level data currently available.
- Estimates of future water levels, either:
  - a) during the design life of the structure, or
  - b) a return to the original (pre-pumping) levels, or
  - c) prevention of the rise of groundwater higher than some present level (either by local pumping or future public policy).
- Measures to avoid the problems detailed in A3.1 and A3.2 relevant to new construction.
- How interpretation of site investigation findings and recommendations could be modified by the anticipation of rising groundwater.
- Additional active precautions.

A2.2   Construction considerations

- Predictability of conditions during the construction period.
- The effects of water ingress and/or pressure on the stability of bored pile shafts, diaphragm walls and excavations.
- Selection of suitable construction techniques based on consideration of future effects, not on past experience in different conditions.
- Temporary pumping and measures to prevent flotation.
- Monitoring of water levels during construction.

A2.3   Maintenance

Maintenance of the required internal environment may require:

- provision for increased active precautions
- more frequent checks on drained cavities and/or external drainage
- monitoring differential settlement.

A3   CONSIDERATIONS FOR EXISTING BASEMENTS

Not all structures within identified critical geographical areas are likely to be affected. The local geology is important as well as the depth and type of construction.

A3.1   Types of structure that are likely to be affected

The types of structure most likely to be affected include:

- structures with deep piles
- exceptionally deep structures
- structures with shallow foundations and shallow basements
- structures with deep basements with shallow under-reamed piles
- victorian brick structures on fill with poorly constructed stone column foundations
- bored piles with excessive loading
- structures with perimeter diaphragm retaining walls connected to basement floors supported on shallow under-reamed piles
- adjacent shallow and deep foundations sensitive to differential movements, i.e. buildings with more than one form of foundation construction.

A3.2 Potential problems for specific elements

These include:

- foundation failures where different forms of construction are used
- differential settlement
- swelling and heave under slabs
- increased forces on propping slabs, rafts and piles
- tensile failure of piles
- drainage layers becoming inadequate necessitating increased pumping, leak sealing and/or new drainage systems
- disruption to passive protection from ground swelling
- increased risk of sulphate attack on concrete
- changes in extent of saline intrusion - although chloride concentrations may eventually fall
- increased risks of methane explosion on, or adjacent to, landfill sites
- flotation.

A3.3 Appraisal of problems

- Carry out a detailed geotechnical appraisal of the building and its specific site conditions.
- Monitor groundwater levels in the vicinity of the building.
- Monitor future building movement for detection of swelling effects.

A3.4 Remedial measures

Remedial works to compensate for rising groundwater level are similar to the repair methods of Chapter 5 and may include:

- grouting of coarse granular soils, e.g. under shallow foundations to prevent differential settlement
- provision of additional drainage or heave space below floor slabs
- grouting to reduce leakage at damaged waterstops
- provision of adequate drainage and water disposal/pumping systems or upgrading of existing active measures
- provision of pressure relief wells.

REFERENCES

A.1   SIMPSON, B., BLOWER, T., CRAIG, R.N. and WILKINSON, W.B.
       The engineering implications of rising groundwater levels in the deep aquifer beneath London
       CIRIA, Special Publication 69, 1989; Executive summary also reproduced separately, 1989

A.2   KNIPE, C.V., LLOYD, J.W., LERNER, D.N. and GRESWELL, R.
       Rising groundwater levels in birmingham and the engineering implications
       CIRIA, Special Publication 92, 1993

Appendix B Comparison of British Standards used in the design of basements

B1 INTRODUCTION

Currently there is no single code for basement design. The principal British Standards associated with the design of reinforced concrete basements are:

BS8110: Parts 1 & 2: 1985 — *Structural use of concrete*
BS8007: 1987 — *Design of concrete structures for retaining aqueous liquids*
BS8102: 1990 — *Protection of structures against water from the ground*

The principal documents associated with the design of plain concrete and masonry basements are:

The Building Regulations 1991 — (effective from June 1992 and the Approved Documents).
BS5628: 1985 — *Use of masonry*
BS8102: 1990 — *Protection of structures against water from the ground*

The elements of design considered are those that directly affect the water resistance of a basement, namely materials properties, cracking, construction joints, movement joints, waterproofing treatments and drainage. Comparison of the requirements in the above documents is given in Tables B.1 for concrete basements and B.2 for masonry basements, (situated at the end of this appendix). Summaries of the important features are given below in Sections B2 and B3.

The designer must give thought to the overall shape of the structure. He should aim at producing the simplest possible plan shape, which serves the intended purpose, and the simplest possible shape of individual elements. Emphasis should be placed on simplicity, 'buildability' and durability. Complicated sections, of walls and slabs, are difficult to shutter, reinforce and concrete satisfactorily and often lead to undesirable concentrations of shrinkage and thermal stresses. Where it is not possible to design the basement as a simple box, considerable and detailed attention must be paid to the design of the passive precautions at sudden changes in slab or wall direction and thickness. In addition the use of 'buildability' aids, such as reinforcement couplers, may also be considered.

B2 CONCRETE BASEMENTS: BS8110: 1985, BS8007: 1987 AND BS8102: 1990

Refer to Table B.1 for details of individual clauses.

B2.1 General

BS8110 states that '*water retaining structures...are more appropriately covered by other codes*'. BS8007 provides recommendations for the design and construction of normal reinforced and prestressed concrete structures used for the containment or exclusion of aqueous liquids but '*does not cover...the damp-proofing of basements*'. BS8102 continues beyond BS8007 by providing '*guidance on methods of dealing with and preventing the entry of water from surrounding ground into a building below ground level*'.

B2.2   Properties of materials

The properties of materials govern the permeability of the basement to water and vapour and also the durability of the construction. For a concrete basement, design of the concrete mix is important, as a compromise must be made between the conflicting requirements of strength, high workability, high aggregate/cement ratio (to minimise early thermal and shrinkage cracking), low water/cement ratio (to ensure low permeability), and economy.

BS8110 covers good design practice for durability in some detail, while BS8007 is more concerned with the permeability of the concrete, and gives guidance on concrete specification.

BS8007 recommends designing for severe exposure conditions with not less than 40 mm cover to the reinforcement and grade C35A concrete (i.e. with a 28-day characteristic compressive cube strength of 35 N/mm²). It is stated that this classification is not in accordance with BS8110, as high 28-day strengths may, with some types and proportions of constituent materials, lead to undesirably high cement contents. A reduction in water/cement ratio may be achieved by the use of plasticisers. Spacing of reinforcement (to control cracking) is important, and it is strongly advised that the design recommendations for area and spacing are followed.

BS8102 introduces the concept of 'construction' (protection) types and providing an impervious membrane to prevent penetration for the protection of concrete, and emphasises the importance of workmanship in achieving high-quality concrete.

B2.3   Cracks

It is important to control the width and occurrence of cracking in concrete structures for all three protection types (Type A, B and C), but particularly in Type B. Early thermal cracking caused by restrained contraction or warping of the concrete as it cools immediately after pouring is generally more serious and occurs more frequently than cracks due to applied loads or resulting from shrinkage or thermal differentials in service. The guidelines to limit cracking are given by BS8110 and are provided in the form of detailing rules deemed to satisfy the provisions in Part 1, and a calculation method with tables to assist in the estimation of the early thermal crack width in Part 2. A calculated maximum crack width of 0.3 mm is generally recommended. This calculated crack width has an acceptably small chance of being exceeded: i.e. a small number of larger cracks may occasionally be expected. Further detailed consideration of the variability of cracking due to bending and restraint of shrinkage or temperature movements is given by Beeby in CIRIA Technical Note 136[B1] and Harrison in CIRIA Report 91[B2].

BS8007, specifically related to water-excluding structures, recommends limiting calculated maximum crack widths to 0.2 mm or 0.1 mm, according to defined circumstances.

BS8102 deals more generally with the overall design of basements, and anticipates that membranes for Type A protection should be capable of accommodating cracks in structures of up to 0.6 mm. Elsewhere in the document it assumes that concrete structures will be within the serviceability crack width limit specified in either BS8110 or BS8007 (according to the environmental grade, determined by its usage). It specifically recommends that Grade 1 basements in Type B structures may be subject to calculated crack widths not exceeding 0.3 mm, in accordance with BS8110: Part 2. Grades 2,3 and 4 basements should be subject to calculated crack widths not exceeding 0.2 mm, in accordance with BS8007.

B2.4   Construction joints

Detailed consideration of the position and treatment of construction joints is furnished by BS8110. This is not developed much further by BS8007, which states '*It is not necessary to incorporate waterstops in properly constructed construction joints*'. BS8102 recommends the use of waterstops. (The recommendations and advice given for construction joints should also be applied to partial contraction joints). See also Sections 3.7.2.5 and 7.4.

B2.5   Movement joints

BS8110 gives guidance on the calculation of movement in a structure and on where to provide joints, in addition to descriptions of contraction, expansion, hinged and settlement joints. BS8007 introduces the partial contraction joint, discusses the spacing of the joints, and fully describes joint fillers, waterstops and joint-sealing compounds. BS8102 does not develop the provisions of BS8007, except to say that allowance should be made in tanking details for substrate movement.

B2.6   'Waterproofing' treatments

'Waterproofing' treatments are not covered by either BS8110 or BS8007, but are discussed in detail in BS8102. The different types of materials are described and general good practice given on preparing a structure for tanking.

B2.7   Drainage

BS8110 recognises the need for exposed surfaces to be freely drained. Drainage is not covered by BS8007. General good practice is given in BS8102.

B3   MASONRY BASEMENTS: BUILDING REGULATIONS 1991 (AND APPROVED DOCUMENTS), BS5628: 1985 AND BS8102: 1990

Refer to Table B.2 for details of individual clauses.

B3.1   General

The Building Regulations state that *'the walls, floors and roof of the building structure should adequately resist the passage of moisture to the inside of the building'*, but do not specifically deal with basements. Prevention of the ingress of moisture for masonry structures is principally dealt with in BS5628: Part 3. The code does not, however, specifically deal with basements, and emphasis is placed on durability of the building materials. BS8102 provides guidance on methods of *'dealing with and preventing the entry of water from surrounding ground into a building below ground level'*.

B3.2   Materials properties

The Building Regulations Approved Document C4 recommends particular concrete mixes as a minimum measure to avoid rising damp in ground floor slabs.

BS5628, however, is more concerned with the durability of the masonry and states that *'particular attention should be paid to the choice of masonry units and mortar...below DPC'*. Readers are warned to take precautions for the prevention of sulphate attack and a table of suitable masonry units and mortar mix designs for use below ground is given.

BS8102 introduces the concept of providing an impervious membrane for the protection of masonry and stresses the importance of workmanship in achieving high quality.

B3.3   Cracks

The Building Regulations (and Approved Documents) do not mention cracks. BS5628 deals with cracks only as associated with subsidence, stress concentrations or other unforeseen movement. BS8102 deals generally with the overall design of a basement to minimise movement and cracking.

B3.4 Construction joints

Not applicable to masonry construction.

B3.5 Movement joints

The Building Regulations do not make reference to movement joints. BS5628 discusses the provision of movement joints and suitable sealing materials. BS8102 does not develop the provisions of BS5628, except to say that allowance should be made in tanking details for substrate movement.

B3.6 'Waterproofing' treatments

The Building Regulations Approved Documents recommend the sealing of structures in contaminated ground with an impermeable barrier, otherwise the provision of at least a 1200 gauge (300 μm) polyethylene sheet under ground slabs (except where liquid waste containing solvents may occur). Where this is not possible, such as around piles (where detailing is critical), alternative measures may be negotiated with the local authority. Provisions for membranes laid above floor slabs and under suspended floor slabs are also covered.

BS5628 is principally concerned with damp-proofing of structures that do not extend below the ground, although the waterproofing of retaining walls is discussed with regard to durability.

'Waterproofing' treatments are discussed in detail in BS8102. Different types of materials are described and general good practice given on preparing a structure for, and the application of tanking.

B3.7 Drainage

The importance of good drainage is recognised by both the Building Regulations Approved Documents and BS5628. However, neither offers detailed advice on the subject. BS8102 gives some guidance.

REFERENCES

B1   BEEBY, A.W.
      Fixings in cracked concrete: The probability of coincident occurrence and likely crack width
      CIRIA Technical Note 136, 1990

B2   HARRISON, T.A.
      Early-age thermal crack control in concrete
      CIRIA Report 91, 1993

Table B1 Interrelationship between the standards for the design of reinforced concrete basements

Subject	BS8110: 1985 Structural use of concrete Part 1 Code of practice for design and construction Part 2 Code of practice for special circumstances	BS8007: 1987 Design of concrete structures for retaining aqueous liquids	BS8102: 1990 Protection of structures against water from the ground
1. General	1.1 Scope 'This Part of BS8110 gives recommendations for the structural use of concrete in building and structures, excluding bridges and structural concrete made with high alumina cement.' Section three. Design and detailing: reinforced concrete NOTE 'Bridges, water-retaining structures, chimneys and some other structures are more appropriately covered by other codes.' **Part 2** 1.1 Scope 'This Part of BS8110 gives recommendations for the design and construction of structural concrete that arise in special circumstances and are not covered in BS8110: Part 1.'	1.1 Scope 'This British Standard provides recommendations for the design and construction of normal reinforced and prestressed concrete structures used for the containment or exclusion of aqueous liquids'... 'The code does not cover dams, pipes, pipelines, lined structures, or the damp-proofing of basements'.	1. Scope 'This Code of Practice provides guidance on methods of dealing with and preventing the entry of water from surrounding ground into a building below ground level. The main methods described are the use of applied waterproofing finishes, watertight construction and drained cavity construction.' 3.2.4 Water resisting forms of construction and 5.1 Structural aspects 'This Code contains recommendations for either minimizing or preventing the entry of water to the inner surfaces of basements and identifies three different types of construction'. (a) 'Type A (Tanked protection). Constructed from concrete or masonry and offering no protection against the ingress of water and water vapour by the nature of its design.' (b) 'Type B (Structurally integral protection). Designed and constructed in reinforced or prestressed concrete either to BS8110 or to BS8007 (to minimize water penetration) or to BS8007 (to prevent water penetration) dependent on the chosen Grade of basement use. Transmission of water vapour may not be wholly prevented'. (c) 'Type C (Drained protection). Constructed from structural concrete (including diaphragm walls) or masonry to minimize the ingress of water. Any moisture which does find its way into the basement is channelled, collected and discharged within the cavity created through the addition of an inner skin to both walls and floor. Vapour transmission may be prevented by ventilation of the cavity and by providing an effective damp proof membrane over the under drained floor'.

Table B1 Interrelationship between the standards for the design of reinforced concrete basements

Subject	BS8110: 1985 Structural use of concrete — Part 1 Code of practice for design and construction — Part 2 Code of practice for special circumstances		BS8007: 1987 Design of concrete structures for retaining aqueous liquids		BS8102: 1990 Protection of structures against water from the ground	
2. Concrete durability	2.1.2 Design method	'...Calculations alone do not produce safe, serviceable and durable structures. Suitable materials, quality control and good supervision are equally important.'	2.7.4 Durability	Mix design and other durability recommendations given should meet the durability requirements of severe exposure as defined in table 3.4 of BS8110: Part 1: 1985. The effects of groundwater on durability of materials should also be considered.	3.1.1 Pre-design considerations	'Where high concentrations of sulphate or other aggressive conditions are found, consideration should be given to the provision of an external impervious membrane or to the use of special cements, both in the structure and in any internal waterproofing, so as to provide adequate resistance to attack. Otherwise normal concrete or sound brickwork are as adequate for below ground use in saturated conditions as they are in standard foundations'.
	2.2.4 Durability	'The environmental conditions to which the concrete will be exposed should be defined at the design stage.' Concrete mixes should be of appropriate quality to the application and coatings may be considered to enhance the durability of vulnerable parts of the construction. 'Good workmanship, particularly curing, is essential and dimensional tolerances and the levels of control and inspection of construction should be specified.'	2.7.5 Impermeability of the concrete	'The concrete shall have low permeability. This is important not only for its direct effect on leakage but also because it is one of the main factors influencing durability; resistance to leaching, chemical attack, erosion, abrasion, frost damage and the protection from corrosion of embedded steel.' Guidance is given on how to achieve low-permeability concrete.	3.1.2 New construction	'Basements of reinforced or prestressed concrete, if properly designed and constructed, will resist the penetration of water under a pressure many times in excess of that normally encountered. Water has the capacity, however, of penetrating even minor defects and a high standard of workmanship is required if the structure is to be completely watertight'.
	3.3.4.1 Exposure conditions	Table 3.2 defines five exposure conditions for concrete.	2.7.6 Cover	'The nominal cover of concrete for all steel...should be not less than 40 mm. A greater cover may be necessary at a face in contact with aggressive soils...'	6.2 Design considerations	Type B structures. 'Cover to reinforcement on the external face should be determined in accordance with severe conditions of exposure as defined in table 3.4 of BS8110: Part 1: 1985. Where aggressive soils are present the specification of concrete quality should comply with table 6.1 of BS8110: Part 1: 1985'. 'Where circumstances dictate section thicknesses less than 250 mm, and in consequence the recommended cover cannot be achieved, consideration should be given to the use of galvanized, epoxy coated, or stainless steel reinforcement'. '...to prevent the ingress of water reinforced concrete design and construction should comply with BS8007 and elements should be so proportioned that concrete strengths and maximum cement contents referred to therein be adhered to'.
	3.3.5.1 Mix proportions	Cover, maximum water cement ratio, minimum cement contents and lowest grade are tabulated (Table 3.4) for concrete for use in given environments.	6.3 Mix proportions	Mix proportions suitable for water-retaining structures are given. 'The 28-day characteristic cube strength should not be less than 35 N/mm², and the concrete should be classed as grade C35A'.		
	3.3.5.5 Use of pulverized-fuel ash (p.f.a) or ground blastfurnace slag (g.g.b.f.s)	'Durability is related to impermeability as well as strength and hence curing is particularly important.'				

Table B1 Interrelationship between the standards for the design of reinforced concrete basements

Subject	BS8110: 1985 Structural use of concrete Part 1 Code of practice for design and construction Part 2 Code of practice for special circumstances		BS8007: 1987 Design of concrete structures for retaining aqueous liquids	BS8102: 1990 Protection of structures against water from the ground
2. Concrete durability (cont.)	6.2.1 General	'One of the main characteristics influencing the durability of concrete is its permeability to the ingress of water, oxygen, carbon dioxide and other potentially deleterious substances. Permeability is governed by the constituents and procedures used in making the concrete'. The degree of exposure should be considered as it will influence the mix design - specification of the concrete should also take account of BS5328.		
	6.2.2. Design for durability	'Since many processes of deterioration of concrete only occur in the presence of free water, the structure should be designed, wherever possible, to minimise uptake of water or exposure to moisture.' 'Concrete is more vulnerable to deterioration due to chemical or climatic attack when it is in thin sections, in sections under hydrostatic pressure from one side only, in partly immersed sections and at corners and edges of elements. The life of the structure can be lengthened by providing extra cover to steel at the corners, by chamfering the corners or by using circular cross sections or by using surface coatings which prevent or reduce the ingress of water, carbon dioxide or aggressive chemicals'.		
	6.2.3.3 Exposure to aggressive chemicals	'Deterioration of concrete by chemical attack can occur by contact with gases or solutions of many chemicals, but it is generally the result of exposure to acidic solutions or to solutions of sulphate salts.' Recommendations for concrete mixes to resist sulphates and acids are given.		

II:159

Table B1 Interrelationship between the standards for the design of reinforced concrete basements

Subject	BS8110: 1985 Structural use of concrete — Part 1 Code of practice for design and construction / Part 2 Code of practice for special circumstances		BS8007: 1987 Design of concrete structures for retaining aqueous liquids		BS8102: 1990 Protection of structures against water from the ground	
3. Cracks	2.2.3.4.1 Reinforced concrete	'Cracking should be kept within reasonable bounds by attention to detail'. This will normally be achieved by compliance with 3.12.11 and, where specific attention is required to limit design crack widths, Part 2 Section 3.2.4.	2.2.3.3 Cracking	Maximum design surface crack width for direct tension and flexure or restrained temperature and moisture effects for reinforced concrete in severe or very severe exposure is 0.2 mm and where appearance is critical 0.1 mm.	5 Structures requiring protection against water and water vapour protection	
	2.2.3.4.2 Prestressed concrete and 4.1.3 Serviceability classification	Structures are classified on the amount of flexural tensile stress allowed under service load as follows: 'Class 1: no flexural tensile stresses; Class 2: flexural stress but no visible cracking; Class 3: flexural tensile stress but surface width of cracks not exceeding 0.1 mm for members in very severe environments (e.g. exposure to sea or moorland water) and not exceeding 0.2 mm for all other members'.	2.5.1 General movement	'Ground movement leading to displacement and cracking of liquid-retaining structures may cause severe leakage'. Guidance is given on design provisions if movement is expected.	5.1.1 General	'Type A structures should be designed to avoid movement or cracks which could damage or overstress the impervious membrane and should provide a firm, smooth and continuous support so that the water pressure is transferred directly through the membrane to the load bearing structure without distortion of the membrane'. 'Cracks, other than hair line cracks, which occur before the application of the membrane, should be made good'.
			2.6.2. Temperature and moisture effects	The origins and methods of control of temperature and moisture effects are discussed. Minimum reinforcement in two directions at right angles within each surface zone should be not less than 0.35% of the surface zone cross-section for grade 460 reinforcement and 0.64% for grade 250.	5.1.2 Reinforced concrete	'Special attention should be given to the provision of sufficient reinforcement to control cracking in accordance with the recommendations of BS8110: Part 1'.
	3.9.4.19 Cracking of concrete	'Reinforcement may be needed in walls to control cracking due to flexure or thermal and hydration shrinkage'... 'Wherever provided, the quantity of reinforcement should be in each direction at least: (a) for grade 460 and above: 0.25% of the concrete cross-sectional area. (b) for grade 250: 0.30% of the concrete cross-sectional area'.	2.7.3 Exposure and appearance	Both faces of a liquid-containing or liquid-excluding structural member and any internal walls and columns of a containment structure are to be considered as subject to severe exposure. Surfaces subjected to very severe exposure should be designed for maximum crack widths of 0.2 mm.	6 Structures in watertight construction	
					6.1 General	'The design should ensure the prevention of differential settlement, the control of cracking and the provision of a dense impervious concrete structure'.
	3.9.4.20 'Anticrack' reinforcement in external plain walls	'...should be provided in both horizontal and vertical directions. It should consist of small diameter bars, relatively closely spaced, with adequate cover near the exposed surface'.	3.2.2 Crack widths	Advice is given on when to apply Appendices A and B, which detail the calculation of crack widths. '...An occasional wider crack in a completed structure should not necessarily be regarded as evidence of excessive local damage unless other factors, such as leakage or appearance, contribute to its unacceptability'.	6.2 Design considerations	'Wall and floor thicknesses should not be less than 250 mm with reinforcement percentages assessed on a serviceability crack width limit state'. 'For grade 1 basements, design should be to BS8110: Part 2 with calculated crack widths not exceeding 0.3 mm'. 'For grade 2, 3 and 4 basements...reinforced concrete design and construction should comply with BS8007'.

Table B1 Interrelationship between the standards for the design of reinforced concrete basements

Subject	BS8110: 1985 Structural use of concrete Part 1 Code of practice for design and construction Part 2 Code of practice for special circumstances	BS8007: 1987 Design of concrete structures for retaining aqueous liquids	BS8102: 1990 Protection of structures against water from the ground
3. Cracks (cont.)	3.12.5.3 Minimum percentages of reinforcement — A table (Table 3.27) of minimum percentages of reinforcement for crack control is given.	Formulae are given for the calculation of reinforcement required to control restrained shrinkage and thermal movement control.	7 Structures with internal drainage 7.1 General '…in grades 3 and 4 basements the reinforced concrete should be designed in accordance with BS8110 and comply with the recommendations of clauses 5 and 6 of this code'.
	3.12.11.2 Spacing of reinforcement — A table (Table 3.30), formulae and other rules are given for calculating minimum reinforcement spacing.	Appendix A Calculation of minimum reinforcement, crack spacing and crack widths, in relation to temperature and moisture effects	
	3.12.11.2.1 General — '…where the limitation of crack widths to 0.3 mm is appropriate, unless the calculation of crack widths (see 3.8 of BS8110: Part 2: 1985) shows that a greater spacing is acceptable, the bar spacing given in 3.12.11.2.2 to 3.12.11.2.9 may be used for beams and slabs where the cover does not exceed 50 mm. Where other conditions apply see BS8110: Part 2'.	Appendix B Calculation of crack widths in mature concrete	
	3.12.11.2.9 Spacing of shrinkage reinforcement — 'When reinforcement is needed to distribute cracking arising from shrinkage and temperature effects, the recommendations given in 3.9.4.19 and 3.9.4.20 for plain walls should be followed'.	Formulae are given for the calculation of crack widths due to applied loads effects.	
	Part 2		
	3.2.4 Excessive cracking — Calculated maximum crack widths should not exceed 0.3 mm for visible members and where there is a risk of corrosion of the reinforcement.		
	3.2.4.3 Loss of performance — 'Where cracking may impair the performance of the structure e.g. watertightness, limits other than those given in 3.2.4.1 and 3.2.4.2 may be appropriate'.		

Table B1 Interrelationship between the standards for the design of reinforced concrete basements

Subject	BS8110: 1985 Structural use of concrete — Part 1 Code of practice for design and construction — Part 2 Code of practice for special circumstances		BS8007: 1987 Design of concrete structures for retaining aqueous liquids		BS8102: 1990 Protection of structures against water from the ground	
3. Cracks (cont.)	3.8 Calculation of crack width	Advice is given on calculation of crack width and bar spacing.				
4. Construction joints	3.12.2.1 Construction joints	'Careful consideration should be given to the location of construction joints and their position agreed before concreting. They should generally be at right angles to the direction of the member. If special preparation of the joint faces is required, it should be specified'.	5.4 Construction joints	The treatment of construction joints is discussed in detail. Full structural continuity is assumed. 'It is not necessary to incorporate waterstops in properly constructed construction joints'.	5.1.4 Plain concrete and masonry	'The position of construction joints in plain concrete should be specified and shown on the drawings'.
	6.12 Construction joints	The treatment of construction joints is discussed in detail.			6.2 Design considerations	'Waterstops should be used in all construction joints....'.
					Section four. Waterstops	This section details the use of internal or external waterstops, their application and limitations.
5. Movement joints	3.12.2.2 Movement joints	'The location of movement joints should be clearly indicated on the drawings both for the individual members and for the structure as a whole. In general, movement joints in the structure should pass through the whole structure in one plane'.	5.2 Types of joints	The following types of joints are identified and described: expansion, complete contraction, partial contraction, hinged, sliding and construction.	5.1.4 Plain concrete and masonry	'If movement joints are incorporated in a basement which is to be tanked, the tanking design details should incorporate waterproof movement joints at the same positions'.
	6.13 Movement joints	The treatment of movement joints is discussed.	5.3.1 Need for movement joints	The need for joints is described in relation to the risk of cracking due to free contraction and expansion.		
	Part 2 — Section seven. Elastic deformation, creep, drying shrinkage and thermal stresses in concrete	Guidance is given on the calculation of deformations of structural concrete including elastic deformation, creep, drying shrinkage and thermal strains.	5.3.2.1 General	'All movement joints should be designed to accommodate repeated movement of the structure without loss of liquid'. In addition the design '...should also provide for the exclusion of grit and debris that would prevent the closing of the joint. Liquid pressure on the joints should be adequately resisted'.		

Table B1 Interrelationship between the standards for the design of reinforced concrete basements

Subject	BS8110: 1985 Structural use of concrete Part 1 Code of practice for design and construction Part 2 Code of practice for special circumstances		BS8007: 1987 Design of concrete structures for retaining aqueous liquids		BS8102: 1990 Protection of structures against water from the ground	
5. Movement joints (cont.)	Section eight. Movement joints					
	8.1 General	The general function of movement joints is to '...permit controlled movement to occur so as to prevent the build-up of harmful stresses'.	5.3.2.2 Expansion joint	'Waterstops, joint fillers and joint sealing compounds are essential.' Sliding joints may be advantageous.		
	8.2 Need for movement joints	They are required because of movement due to wetting and drying, thermal movement, creep and differential settlements of foundations.	5.3.2.3 Complete contraction joint	'Waterstops are essential as are joint sealing compounds where debris may enter the joints'. Dowel bars may be used with one end free to slide.		
	8.3 Types of movement joint	A full description is given of the following types of movement joint: contraction, expansion, sliding, hinged and settlement.	5.3.3 Spacing of movement joints	The spacing of joints must be carefully designed. There are three options: - design for full restraint - design for partial restraint - design for freedom of movement.		
	8.4 Provision of joints	General advice on the provision of joints is given.	5.6 Joints in ground slabs	To minimise restraints to movement, a separating layer of 1000 g/m² polyethylene should be provided between floor slab and blinding concrete. 'Alternatively, the floor may be designed as fully restrained against shrinkage and thermal contraction and should be cast directly onto the blinding concrete'.		
	8.5 Design of joints	'A movement joint should fulfil all necessary functions. It should possess the merits of simplicity and freedom of movement, yet retain the other appropriate characteristics necessary e.g. weatherproofness, fire resistance, resistance to corrosion, durability and sound insulation'.	Appendix C Jointing materials	Describes joint fillers, waterstops and joint sealing compounds.		
6. Water-resisting materials	6.2.3.3 Exposure to aggressive chemicals	'For the very high sulphate concentrations in class 5 conditions, some form of lining such as sheet polyethylene or polychloroprene, or surface coating based on asphalt, chlorinated rubber, epoxy or polyurethane materials should be used to prevent access by sulphate solution'.		No mention	3.1.2 New construction	'Many basements give the impression of dampness due either to the penetration of moisture or to condensation. Providing the supporting structure is sound, the inclusion of an impervious membrane will resist the former while the provision of adequate ventilation, assisted by heating, coupled with the suitable treatment of floor and wall surfaces will combat the latter'.

Table B1 Interrelationship between the standards for the design of reinforced concrete basements

Subject	BS8110: 1985 *Structural use of concrete* Part 1 *Code of practice for design and construction* Part 2 *Code of practice for special circumstances*	BS8007: 1987 *Design of concrete structures for retaining aqueous liquids*	BS8102: 1990 *Protection of structures against water from the ground*	
6. Water-resisting materials (cont.)			4 Materials	This clause summarises the types of waterproofing material available in sections 4.1 to 4.10.
			4.1.1 General	*'Waterproofing materials are intended to provide a barrier against water. They may also provide resistance to the diffusion of water vapour'.*
			5.1.1 General	*'Although some membranes will accept minimal movement most are damaged by differential movement or cracking of the supporting structure'.* *'A flexible membrane system should be capable of accommodating, without loss of waterproofing, unanticipated cracks of up to 0.6 mm wide and the structure should be designed accordingly'.*
			5.2 Barrier materials	Suitable barrier materials for Type A basements are described.
			9 Mastic asphalt tanking	General good practice on preparing a structure for tanking is given. Consideration is given to externally and internally applied tanking, pumping water from the site, surface preparation and special conditions.
			10 Bitumen sheet tanking	This clause details general good practice on the use of bitumen sheet tanking.
			11 Internally applied cementitious waterproof render	This clause details general good practice on the use of internally applied cementitious waterproof renders.

Table B1 Interrelationship between the standards for the design of reinforced concrete basements

Subject	BS8110: 1985 *Structural use of concrete* Part 1 *Code of practice for design and construction* Part 2 *Code of practice for special circumstances*	BS8007: 1987 *Design of concrete structures for retaining aqueous liquids*	BS8102: 1990 *Protection of structures against water from the ground*	
6. Water resisting materials (cont.)			12 Polyurethane resin tanking	This clause details general good practice on the use of polyurethane resin tanking.
			13 Self-adhesive rubber bitumen membrane tanking system	This clause details general good practice on the use of self-adhesive rubber bitumen membrane tanking system.
7. Drainage	2.2.4 Durability — '...the need to ensure that surfaces exposed to water are freely draining'.	No mention	3.2.2 Exclusion of surface water	'Wherever possible, rainwater should be prevented from soaking into the ground adjoining any basement. This may be achieved by one of the following methods. *(a) Arranging for the adjoining ground surface to slope away from the structure for about 3 m and provide sufficient transverse gradient to avoid ponding. (b) On sloping sites of where the gradient of the ground surface adjoining the 3 m strip is adverse, construct a cut-off land drain to intercept approaching surface water to conduct it to a lower level. (c) Where possible, pave the 3 m strip and take its surface water run-off...for disposal well clear of the structure.* BS8301 gives recommendations on collecting and disposing of surface and subsoil water'.
			3.2.3 Subsurface drainage	'Any existing system of land drains should be most carefully preserved'. Guidance on design of subsoil drainage is given.

Table B2 Interrelationship between the Building Regulations 1991 (Approved 1992) and British Standards for the design of plain concrete and masonry basements

Subject	The Building Regulations 1991 (Approved Documents 1992)	BS5628: 1985 Use of masonry (Part 3 unless otherwise stated)	BS8102: 1990 Protection of structures against water from the ground
1. General	**Requirement C4 Resistance to weather and ground moisture.** 'The walls, floor and roof of the building shall adequately resist the passage of moisture to the inside of the building'.	**Part 1** — 1 Scope — 'The thickness of a wall determined from strength considerations may not always be sufficient to satisfy requirements for other properties such as... resistance to damp penetration and reference should be made to BS5628: Part 3 or BS5390.'	1 Scope — 'This Code of Practice provides guidance on methods of dealing with and preventing the entry of water from surrounding ground into a building below ground level. The main methods described are the use of applied waterproofing finishes, watertight construction and drained cavity construction.'
	Performance 'In the Secretary of State's view the requirement of C4 will be met by: a. a floor next to the ground preventing undue moisture from reaching the upper surface of the floor. b. a wall preventing undue moisture from the ground reaching the inside of the building, and, if it is an outside wall, adequately resisting the penetration of rain and snow to the inside of the building... d. ensuring that floors next to the ground, walls and roof are not damaged by moisture from the ground, rain or snow and do not carry that moisture to any part of the building which it would damage.'	**Part 3** — 1 Scope — 'This part of BS5628 gives general recommendations for the design and construction of brick and block masonry, including materials and components, the main aspects of design, other than structural, which is covered by BS5628: Parts 1 and 2, and workmanship.' This code does not cover natural stone masonry.'	3.2.4 Water-resisting forms of construction and 5.1 Structural aspects 'This Code contains recommendations for either minimizing or preventing the entry of water to the inner surfaces of basements and identifies three different types of construction: (a) 'Type A (Tanked protection). Constructed from concrete or masonry and offering no protection against the ingress of water and water vapour by the nature of its design.' (b) 'Type B (Structurally integral protection)'. Constructed in reinforced or prestressed concrete only. (c) 'Type C (Drained protection). Constructed from structural concrete (including diaphragm walls) or masonry to minimize the ingress of water. Any moisture which does find its way into the basement is channelled, collected and discharged within the cavity created through the addition of an inner skin to both walls and floor. Vapour transmission may be prevented by ventilation of the cavity and by providing an effective damp proof membrane over the under drained floor'.
	Section 3 Floors next to the ground		
	3.2 A floor next to the ground should: 'a. resist ground moisture from reaching the upper surface of the floor... b. not be damaged by moisture from the ground'.		

Table B2 Interrelationship between the Building Regulations 1991 (Approved 1992) and British Standards for the design of plain concrete and masonry basements

Subject	The Building Regulations 1991 (Approved Documents 1992)		BS5628: 1985 *Use of masonry* (Part 3 unless otherwise stated)	BS8102: 1990 *Protection of structures against water from the ground*
1. General (cont.)	Technical solution			
	3.4	'A concrete ground supported floor may be built as follows (unless it is subjected to water pressure...)... b. concrete at least 100 mm thick (but thicker if the structural design requires) and composed of 50 kg of cement to not more than 0.11 m^3 of fine aggregate and 0.16 m^3 of coarse aggregate or BS5328, mix ST2. If there is embedded steel, the concrete should be composed of 50 kg of cement and not more than 0.08 m^3 of fine aggregate and 0.13 m^3 of coarse aggregate or BS5328 mix ST4...'		
	Alternative approach			
	3.8	'The performance...can also be achieved by following the relevant recommendations of Clause 11 of CP 102: 1973 Protection of buildings against water from the ground. BS8102: 1990 Code of practice for protection of structures against water from the ground includes recommendations for floors subject to water pressure'.		
	Suspended timber ground floors			
	Technical solution			
	3.10	'A suspended timber floor next to the ground may be built as follows...(unless it is covered with a floor finish which is highly vapour resistant...) a. ground covering either- i. concrete at least 100 mm thick composed of 50 kg of cement to not more than 0.13 m^3 of fine aggregate and 0.18 m^3 of coarse aggregate or BS5328 mix ST1 if there is no embedded steel...'		

Table B2 Interrelationship between the Building Regulations 1991 (Approved 1992) and British Standards for the design of plain concrete and masonry basements

Subject	The Building Regulations 1991 (Approved Documents 1992)	BS5628: 1985 Use of masonry (Part 3 unless otherwise stated)	BS8102: 1990 Protection of structures against water from the ground
1. General (cont.)	ii. concrete composed as described above or inert fine aggregate, in either case at least 50 mm thick laid on at least 300μm (1200 gauge) polyethylene (polythene) sheet with the joints sealed on a bed of material which will not damage the sheet'.		
	Suspended concrete ground floors		
	3.13 'A suspended concrete floor may be built as follows:		
	a. in-situ concrete at least 100 mm thick (but thicker if the structural design requires) containing at least 300 kg of cement for each m³ of concrete, or		
	b. precast concrete construction with or without infilling slabs, and		
	c. reinforcing steel protected by concrete cover of at least 40 mm if the concrete is in-situ and at least the thickness required for a moderate exposure if the concrete is precast'.		
	Walls		
	4.2 'Walls should:		
	a. resist the passage of moisture from the ground to the inside of the building...and		
	b. not be damaged by moisture from the ground and not carry moisture from the ground to any part which would be damaged by it'.		

Table B2 Interrelationship between the Building Regulations 1991 (Approved 1992) and British Standards for the design of plain concrete and masonry basements

Subject	The Building Regulations 1991 (Approved Documents 1992)		BS5628: 1985 Use of masonry (Part 3 unless otherwise stated)	BS8102: 1990 Protection of structures against water from the ground
1. General (cont.)	Internal and external walls (moisture from the ground)			
	4.3	'Any internal or external wall will meet the performance if a damp-proof course is provided'.		
	Technical solution			
	4.4	'Any internal or external wall may be built as follows (unless it is subjected to ground water pressure...)... a. damp-proof course of bituminous material, engineering bricks or slates in cement mortar or other material that will prevent the passage of moisture. The damp-proof course should be continuous with any damp-proof membrane in floors...'.		
	Alternative approach			
	4.5	'The performance can also be met by following the relevant recommendations of Clauses 4 & 5 of BS8215: 1991 Code of practice for design and installation of damp-proof courses in masonry construction. BS8102: 1990 Code of practice for protection of structures against water from the ground includes recommendations for walls subject to ground water pressure including basement walls'.		

Table B2 Interrelationship between the Building Regulations 1991 (Approved 1992) and British Standards for the design of plain concrete and masonry basements

Subject	The Building Regulations 1991 (Approved Documents 1992)	BS5628: 1985 *Use of masonry* (Part 3 unless otherwise stated)	BS8102: 1990 *Protection of structures against water from the ground*
2. Durability of construction materials	**C4** Performance: 'Damage can be avoided either by preventing moisture from getting to materials which would be damaged or by using materials which will not be damaged'.	**17.1 Factors to be considered** — Two of the factors which need to be considered in design are: resistance to rain penetration durability	**3.1.1 Pre-design considerations** — 'Where high concentrations of sulphate or other aggressive conditions are found, consideration should be given to the provision of an external impervious membrane or to the use of special cements, both in the structure and in any internal waterproofing, so as to provide adequate resistance to attack. Otherwise normal concrete or sound brickwork are as adequate for below ground use in saturated conditions as they are in standard foundations'.
	Suspended concrete ground floors — Technical solution	**22 Durability** — This section gives recommendations for durability of masonry construction including a table (Table 13) which gives guidance on the types of masonry units suitable for various applications including work below or near external ground level.	**3.1.2 New construction** — 'Water has the capacity, however, of penetrating even minor defects and a high standard of workmanship is required if the structure is to be completely watertight'.
	3.13 — 'c. reinforcing steel protected by concrete cover of at least 40 mm if the concrete is in-situ and at least the thickness required for moderate exposure if the concrete is precast'.	**22.1 General**	**5.1.4 Plain concrete and masonry** — 'Plain concrete walls should be designed and constructed to comply with the recommendations for mass concrete in Civil Engineering Code of Practice No. 2. Masonry should comply with the special recommendations of Civil Engineering Code of Practice No. 2. Additionally, masonry below damp-proof course should comply with the recommendations of BS5628'.
		22.1.3 — 'The durability of masonry depends only upon the characteristics of the masonry units and the mortar, particularly as regards resistance to frost and chemical attack. The following factors affect the susceptibility of the masonry to damage'. '(a) Exposure to the weather or to other sources of water'. '(b) Exposure to aggressive conditions from all sources including the ground'. '(c) The adequacy of methods taken to prevent the masonry from becoming saturated both in terms of design and workmanship'. 'Particular attention should be paid to the choice of masonry units and mortar...where the masonry is likely to become and may remain saturated for long periods of time'.	**6.2 Structures in watertight construction** — 'Where aggressive soils are present the specification of concrete quality should comply with table 6.1 BS8110: Part 1: 1985'.
		22.4 Sulphate attack — 'The sulphates may be derived from ground waters, and from the ground (including fill adjacent to the masonry)...'.	

Table B2 Interrelationship between the Building Regulations 1991 (Approved 1992) and British Standards for the design of plain concrete and masonry basements

Subject	The Building Regulations 1991 (Approved Documents 1992)	BS5628: 1985 *Use of masonry* (Part 3 unless otherwise stated)	BS8102: 1990 *Protection of structures against water from the ground*
2. Durability of construction materials (cont.)		'The degree to which soluble salts are extracted depends on the quantity of water available and the permeability of the masonry. For this reason, the greatest attention should be given to the provision of effective DPCs and to the exclusion of water by good design and detailing. Where masonry is likely to remain wet for long periods of time e.g.... below DPC at or near ground level,... sulphation of mortar can occur and consideration should be given to the use of strong mixes or of ordinary or sulphate-resisting Portland cement in mortars used in these situations.' **23 Selection of mortars** This section details the durability of mortars and includes a table (Table 15) of mortar mixes related to strength and durability requirements.	
3. Cracks	No mention	**20 Movement in masonry** **20.1 General** 'In general, because restraints are not completely free to expand or contract and compressive forces may develop, and these may lead to bowing or cracking'. 'The risk of cracking is increased where there are stress concentrations, for example at openings or at changes in height, thickness or direction of walls, and where stronger mortars than those recommended in clause 22 are used'.	**5.1.1 General** 'Type A structures should be designed to avoid movement or cracks which could damage or overstress the impervious membrane and should provide a firm, smooth and continuous support so that the water pressure is transferred directly through the membrane to the load bearing structure without distortion of the membrane'. 'Cracks, other than hair line cracks, which occur before the application of the membrane, should be made good. A flexible membrane system should be capable of accommodating, without loss of waterproofing, unanticipated cracks of up to 0.6 mm and the structure should be designed accordingly'.
4. Construction joints	No mention	Not applicable	**5.1.4 Plain concrete and masonry** 'The position of construction joints in plain concrete should be specified and shown on the drawings.' **Section four. Waterstops** This section details the use of waterstops in joints, including internal and external application and their limitations.

Table B2 Interrelationship between the Building Regulations 1991 (Approved 1992) and British Standards for the design of plain concrete and masonry basements

Subject	The Building Regulations 1991 (Approved Documents 1992)	BS5628: 1985 *Use of masonry* (Part 3 unless otherwise stated)	BS8102: 1990 *Protection of structures against water from the ground*
5. Movement joints	No mention	11.0 Sealants — 'Sealants should comply with the relevant British Standard'.	5.1.4 Plain concrete and masonry — 'If movement joints are incorporated in a basement which is to be tanked, the tanking design details should incorporate waterproof movement joints at the same positions.'
		20.3.2 Provision of movement joints — This is discussed with reference to Appendix A, which contains calculations for movement joints in detail.	
		20.4 Sealing of movement joints — The suitability and design of sealants to accommodate movement is discussed.	
6. Water-resisting materials	C2 Contaminants. Signs of contaminants. 2.3 Where the ground is likely to contain contaminants, (some instances which are given in Table 2) the ground may be sealed when '...a suitable imperforate barrier is laid between the contaminant and the building and sealed at the joints, around the edges and at the service entries'.	10.0 Damp-proof courses — 'Materials for damp-proof courses (DPCs) should comply with the relevant British Standard'.	3.1.2 New construction — 'Many basement give the impression of dampness due either to the penetration of moisture or to condensation. Providing the supporting structure is sound, the inclusion of an impervious membrane will resist the former while the provision of adequate ventilation, assisted by heating, coupled with the suitable treatment of floor and wall surfaces will combat the latter'.
		21 Exclusion of moisture — This section discusses the exclusion of moisture resulting from rain penetration. Recommendations on applied external finishes, quality of workmanship, mortar composition, single and double leaf constructions are made.	4 Materials — This clause summarises the types of waterproofing material available in sections 4.1 to 4.10.
	Section 3 Floors next to the ground. Technical solution. 3.4 'c. damp-proof membrane above or below the concrete and continuous with damp proof courses in walls, piers and the like'.	21.3.2 Detailed consideration	
		21.3.2.1 'The use of masonry paint systems...and other proprietary external finishes... e.g. silicone based water repellents...may increase the resistance to rain penetration. However, these surface treatments may also reduce the rate of evaporation of water from the wall and...the quantity of water in the wall may therefore increase'.	4.1.1 General — 'Waterproofing materials are intended to provide a barrier against water. They may also provide resistance to the diffusion of water vapour'.
		21.3.2.6 Unfilled cavity walls — '...in general, designers should not rely on the inner leaf of a cavity wall to resist rain penetration'.	5.1.1 General — 'Although some membranes will accept minimal movement most are damaged by differential movement or cracking of the supporting structure'.
			'A flexible membrane system should be capable of accommodating, without loss of waterproofing, unanticipated cracks of up to 0.6 mm wide and the structure should be designed accordingly'.

Table B2 Interrelationship between the Building Regulations 1991 (Approved 1992) and British Standards for the design of plain concrete and masonry basements

Subject	The Building Regulations 1991 (Approved Documents 1992)	BS5628: 1985 Use of masonry (Part 3 unless otherwise stated)	BS8102: 1990 Protection of structures against water from the ground
6. Water-resisting materials (cont.)	3.5 'A membrane laid below the concrete should be at least 300µm (1200 gauge) polyethylene (e.g. polythene) sheet, laid with the joints sealed, on a bed of material which will not damage the sheet.'	21.4 Damp-proof courses and cavity trays	5.2 Barrier materials — Suitable barrier materials for Type A basements are described.
			9 Mastic asphalt tanking — General good practice on preparing a structure for tanking is given. Consideration is given to externally and internally applied tanking, pumping water from the site, surface preparation and special conditions.
	3.6 'A membrane laid above the concrete should be either polyethylene sheet...or three coats of cold applied bitumen solution or similar moisture and water-vapour resisting material. In each case it should be protected either by a screed or a floor finish, unless the membrane is pitchmastic or similar material which will also serve as a floor finish.'	21.4.1 'A damp-proof course (DPC) in a building is intended to provide a barrier to the passage of water from the exterior of the building to the interior, or from the ground to the structure, or from one part of the structure to another. The passage of water may be horizontal, upwards, or downwards'.	10 Bitumen sheet tanking — This clause details general good practice on the use of bitumen sheet tanking.
			11 Internally applied cementitious waterproof render — This clause details general good practice on the use of internally applied cementitious waterproof renders.
	3.8 'The performance...can also be achieved by following the relevant recommendations of Clause 11 of CP102: 1973 Protection of buildings against water from the ground. BS8102: 1990 Code of practice for protection of structures against water from the ground includes recommendations for floors subject to water pressure'.	22.1 General; 22.1.3 Where sections of wall are acting as earth retaining '...there is an increased risk of frost and sulphate attack, efflorescence, lime leaching and staining of the waterproofing of the outer leaf. The application of a waterproofing treatment to the face of the masonry in contact with the ground will minimise or obviate such problems.'	12 Polyurethane resin tanking — This clause details general good practice on the use of polyurethane resin tanking.
			13 Self-adhesive rubber bitumen membrane tanking system — This clause details general good practice on the use of self-adhesive rubber bitumen membrane tanking system.
Suspended timber ground floors			
Technical solution	3.10 'c. damp-proof courses of impervious sheet material, engineering brick or slates in cement mortar or other material which will prevent the passage of moisture'.		

Table B2 Interrelationship between the Building Regulations 1991 (Approved 1992) and British Standards for the design of plain concrete and masonry basements

Subject	The Building Regulations 1991 (Approved Documents 1992)	BS5628: 1985 *Use of masonry* (Part 3 unless otherwise stated)	BS8102: 1990 *Protection of structures against water from the ground*
6. Water-resisting materials (cont.)	Suspended concrete ground floors Technical solution 3.14 'A suspended concrete floor should incorporate: a. damp-proof membrane (to be provided if the ground below the floor has been excavated below the level of the surrounding ground and will not be effectively drained)...'. Walls Internal and External walls (moisture from the ground) Technical solution 4.4 'An internal or external wall may be built as follows....: a. damp-proof course of bituminous material, engineering bricks or slates in cement mortar or other material that will prevent the passage of moisture. The damp-proof course should be continuous with any damp-proof membrane in the floors....'.		
7. Drainage	Requirement C.3 Subsoil drainage 'Sub-soil drainage shall be provided if it is needed to avoid- (a) the passage of ground water to the interior of the building; (b) damage to the fabric of the building'.	22.1 General 22.1.3 'The degree to which masonry used below DPC, at or near ground level becomes saturated will vary according to the site. The masonry materials will become far less prone to problems on a site that is well drained and dry. Where the site is wet, and/or the masonry at or near ground level may be subject to saturation, particular care should be taken in the choice of materials.'	3.2.2 Exclusion of surface water 'Wherever possible, rainwater should be prevented from soaking into the ground adjoining any basement. This may be achieved by one of the following methods. (a) Arranging for the adjoining ground surface to slope away from the structure for about 3 m and provide sufficient transverse gradient to avoid ponding.'

Table B2 Interrelationship between the Building Regulations 1991 (Approved 1992) and British Standards for the design of plain concrete and masonry basements

Subject	The **Building Regulations 1991** (Approved Documents 1992)		**BS5628: 1985** *Use of masonry* (Part 3 unless otherwise stated)	**BS8102: 1990** *Protection of structures against water from the ground*	
7. Drainage (cont.)	Section 1				(b) On sloping sites of where the gradient of the ground surface adjoining the 3 m strip is adverse, construct a cut-off land drain to intercept approaching surface water to conduct it to a lower level.
	Site preparation and site drainage				
	Site drainage				(c) Where possible, pave the 3 m strip and take its surface water run-off...for disposal well clear of the structure.
	1.5	'Where the water table can rise to within 0.25 m of the lowest floor of the building, or where surface water could enter or adversely affect the building either the ground to be covered by the building should be drained by gravity or by other effective means of safeguarding the building should be taken'.			BS8301 gives recommendations on collecting and disposing of surface and subsoil water'.
				3.2.3 Sub-surface drainage	'Any existing system of land drains should be most carefully preserved'.
					Guidance on design of subsoil drainage is given.
	Alternative approach				
	1.7	'The performance will be met if, as an alternative to providing or re-routing sub-soil drainage, the building is designed and constructed to prevent the passage of ground and surface water to the inside or to materials which would be adversely affected by it'.			

Appendix C   Heating and ventilation requirements

Notes: 1.   The example calculations set out in this Appendix are intended for use by persons familiar with heating and ventilation design.

2.   They do not apply to any specific building. Each basement should be assessed individually and its requirements established.

C1   LIST OF SYMBOLS

Db	=	Dry bulb (thermometer)
Wb	=	Wet bulb (thermometer)
RH	=	Relative humidity (%)
Q	=	Total heating, or cooling, capacity (kW)
m_a	=	Mass flow rate of air (m³/s)
C_p	=	Specific heat capacity or air (kJ/kgK)
ΔT	=	Temperature difference (between the external supply air and internal supply air) (°C)
M	=	Moisture movement through the element (kg/m²s)
P_{vi}	=	Water vapour pressure, internal (kPa)
P_{vo}	=	Water vapour pressure, external (kPa)
r_n	=	Water vapour resistivity of a material, n (GNs/kgm)
d_n	=	Thickness of a layer of material, n (m)
G	=	Vapour resistance of an element made up of one or more materials (kg/m²s)
U-value	=	Thermal transmittance coefficient (W/m²K)
R_{si}	=	Inside surface resistance (m²K/W)
R_{so}	=	Outside surface resistance (m²K/W)
R_n	=	Thermal resistance of a material (mK/W, for a given thickness of material m²K/W)
λ	=	Thermal conductivity of a material (W/mK)
l_n	=	Thickness of a material, n (m)

C2 CALCULATION OF VENTILATION REQUIREMENTS

A series of example calculations for different grades of basement usage are presented.

C2.1 Basement car park

This example demonstrates the calculations necessary to establish the ventilation requirements in a basement used as a car park, assuming a floor area of 1600 m^2 and a floor-to-ceiling height of 2.6 m.

$$Volume = 1600 \times 2.6 \times = 4160 \ m^3$$

Extract ventilation requirements; 6 air changes per hour (see Section 3.9.1).

$$4160 \ m^3 \quad \times \quad \frac{6}{60 \times 60} \quad = \quad 6.9 \ m^3/s$$

If the supply air is taken from the access ramps the designer must advise the owner that solid security doors are not to be installed if there is a possibility of the extract fans operating when the doors are closed.

If the supply air is to be ducted into the area, then the ductwork must be suitably protected from damage by vehicles. This especially applies to low-level ductwork and ductwork running down centrally located columns.

See Figure C.1 for a schematic representation of a typical ventilation scheme for an outdoor design temperature of ¯1 °C.

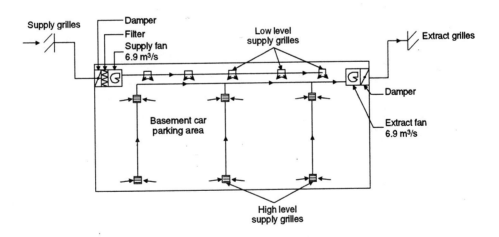

Figure C1   Schematic plan representation of a basement car park ventilation scheme (showing the relationship between the different elements of the system)

C2.2 Basement offices

Assume the design brief for an office is as follows:

■ Dimensions
Area	1600 m^2
Slab - ceiling height	2.7 m
Ceiling void height	0.6 m

- External temperature conditions
  - Summer   29 °C Db, 18 °C Wb
  - Winter   -1 °C Db

- Internal temperature conditions
  - Air-conditioned areas   22 °C Db ± 2 °C, 50% RH ± 10%

- Ventilation requirements   Fresh air introduced through the air conditioning system should be based upon 10 l/s per person.

- Occupancy   1 person per 10 m²

- Heating load estimate   70 W/m²

- Cooling Load Estimate   125 W/m²

Ventilation rate at 6 air changes per hour is

$$1600 \times 2.7 \times \frac{6}{60 \times 60} = 7.2 \ m^3/s$$

A schematic representation of the office heating and air-conditioning scheme is given in Figure C2.

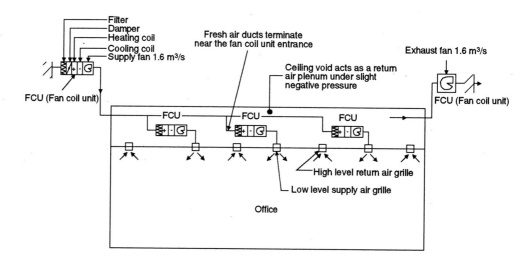

Figure C2 Schematic plan representation of an office heating, ventilation and air-conditioning scheme (showing the relationship between the different elements of the system)

Hence 7.2 m³/s of air is required to be passed through the fan coil units in the ceiling void. From the 7.2 m³/s, the required supply of fresh air to the occupants, is calculated as follows:

1600 m² × 1 person/10 m² × 10 l/s/person = 1600 l/s.

Hence 1.6 m³/s of fresh outdoor air is required, or approximately 20% of the total ventilation rate should be made up of outdoor air.

Assuming that air is constantly supplied at 18 °C, then the total heating capacity (Q) required to raise the temperature of the fresh air can be defined as:

m_a =   mass flow rate of air
C_p =   specific heat capacity of air = 1.03 kJ/kgK
ΔT =   temperature difference between the external supply air and internal supply air.

$$Q = m_a\, C_p\, \Delta T$$
$$= 1.6\ m^3/s \times 1.2\ kg/m^3 \times 1.03\ kJ/kgK \times (18 - 1)$$
$$= 33.6\ kW$$

and the total cooling capacity required by the equipment is:

$$Q = m_a\, C_p\, \Delta T$$
$$= 1.6\ m^3/s \times 1.2\ kg/m^3 \times 1.03\ kJ/kgK \times (18 - 29)$$
$$= 21.7\ kW$$

Additional cooling may be required, depending on the office area usage. Humidification would need to be controlled and operate during the heating period and dehumidification would operate during the cooling period.

C2.3 Archives and stores requiring a totally dry environment

Assume an internal temperature of 13 °C at 35% RH with 3 air changes per hour (see Figure C3 for a schematic representation of a ventilation scheme for an outdoor design temperature of ‾1 °C).

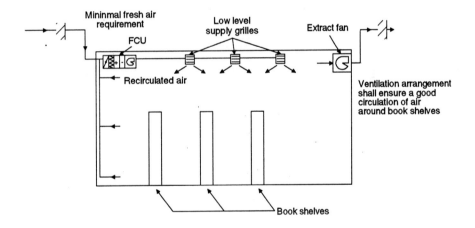

Figure C3 Schematic plan representation of an archive heating, ventilation and air-conditioning scheme (showing the relationship between the different elements of the system)

Fresh air should be based upon the requirements of any occupants.

Dehumidification and cooling would be necessary during the summer months and require specialist equipment. Humidification and heating would be necessary during the winter months.

Care is required when selecting carpets and interior furnishings, to prevent the build-up of static electricity, which is often a problem with dry air conditions.

C3   CALCULATION OF MOISTURE AND THERMAL TRANSMITTANCE

C3.1   Type A protection: concrete construction, Grade 1 basement e.g. car park

This example demonstrates the calculations necessary for moisture and thermal transmittance in the reinforced concrete and membrane walls and floor of the basement car park construction shown in Figure C4.

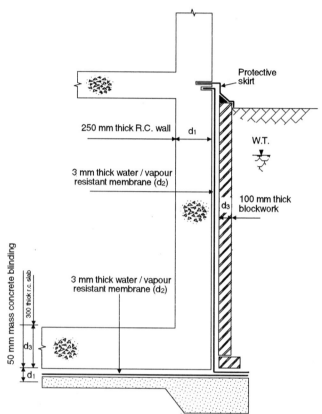

Figure C4 Schematic section through Type A protection (concrete and external membrane) assumed in example calculation for moisture and thermal transmittance
Grade 3 use - Residential
Grade 1 use - Car park (is similar but thinner membrane possible and basement slab with falls to drains)

N.B. Negative values indicate moisture movement <u>into</u> the basement.

C3.1.1   Moisture loss

Moisture loss through a material may be calculated from;

$$M = \frac{P_{vi} - P_{vo}}{G} \quad kg/m^2s$$

for any particular element.

(a)   Moisture loss through wall

Summer: P_{vi} @ 29 °C Db, 20 °C Wb = 1.641 kPa
                P_{vo} @ 5 °C Db and 100% RH = 0.8719 kPa
                $G = r_1 d_1 + r_2 d_2 + r_3 d_3$

Where   concrete $r_1 = 80$ GNs/kgm, $d_1 = 0.25$ m
        water-resistant membrane $r_2 = 1000$ GNs/kgm, $d_2 = 0.003$ m
        blockwork $r_3 = 50$ GNs/kgm, $d_3 = 0.1$ m

$$G = (80 \times 0.25 + 1000 \times 0.003 + 50 \times 0.1) \; GNs/kg = 28 \; GNs/kg$$

$$M = \frac{(1.641 - 0.8719) \times 10^3 \; Pa}{28 \times 10^9 \; Ns/kg}$$

$$= 0.0275 \times 10^{-6} \; kg/m^2s$$

Winter: P_{vi} @ 0 °C Db, 100% RH = 0.6108 kPa

$$M = -0.0093 \times 10^{-6} \; kg/m^2s$$

(b)   Moisture Loss through Floor

where:

$P_{vi} =$ 1.641 kPa (Summer)
$P_{vo} =$ 0.8719 kPa
$G =$ concrete blinding $r_1 = 30,$ $d_1 = 0.05$
                water-resistant membrane $r_2 = 1000,$ $d_2 = 0.003$
                concrete $r_1 = 200,$ $d_3 = 0.3$

$$= 0.012 \times 10^{-6} \; kg/m^2s$$

Winter:

$$M = -0.004 \times 10^{-6} \; kg/m^2s$$

C3.1.2   *Heat loss*

To calculate the heat loss, the U-value of the structure is required. There are strict guidelines, relating to heated buildings, set out in the Building Regulations Approved Document L, 1995 edition, to which the composite structure must adhere regarding permissible U-values for an external basement wall. The U-value must not, in such cases, be greater than 0.45 W/m²K.

(a)   U-value for wall

$$U = \frac{1}{(R_{si} + R_1 + R_2 + R_3 + R_{so})}$$

Where: $R_{si} = 0.12 \; mK/W$
                $R_{so} = 0.12 \; mK/W$

$$R_1 = concrete \; R_1 = \frac{1_1}{\lambda} = \frac{0.25 \; m}{0.44 \; W/mK} = 0.568 \; m^2K/W$$

$$R_2 = \text{waterproof membrane } R_2 = \frac{l_2}{\lambda} = \frac{0.003 \text{ } m}{0.22 \text{ } W/mK} = 0.013 \text{ } m^2K/W$$

$$R_3 = \text{blockwork } R_3 = \frac{l_3}{\lambda} = \frac{0.1 \text{ } m}{0.51 \text{ } W/mK} = 0.196 \text{ } m^2K/W$$

$$U = \frac{1}{(0.12 + 0.568 + 0.013 + 0.196 + 0.12)}$$

$$= \frac{1}{1.017} = 0.983 \text{ } W/m^2K$$

(b)   U-value for floor

$$U = \frac{1}{(0.12 + \dfrac{0.05}{0.2} + \dfrac{0.003}{0.22} + \dfrac{0.3}{0.44} + 0.12)}$$

$$= \frac{1}{1.185} = 0.843 \text{ } W/m^2K$$

C3.2   Type A protection: concrete construction, Grade 3 basement e.g. Residential

This example demonstrates the calculations necessary for moisture and thermal transmittance in the reinforced concrete and membrane walls and floor of the residential basement shown in Figure C4.

> **N.B. Negative values indicate moisture movement <u>into</u> the basement.**

C3.2.1 Moisture loss

Calculated following the principles set out in Section C3.1.1.

(a)   Moisture loss through wall

P_{vi} @ 22 °C Db and 60% RH = 1.602 kPa
P_{vo} @ 5 °C Db and 100% RH = 0.8719 kPa

$$M = \frac{(1.602 - 0.8719) \text{ } x \text{ } 10^3 \text{ } Pa}{28 \text{ } x \text{ } 10^9 \text{ } Ns/kg} \qquad \textit{(refer to example C1.2.1 for G)}$$

$$= 0.026 \text{ } x \text{ } 10^{-6} \text{ } kg/m^2s$$

(b)   Moisture loss through floor

$$M = \frac{(1.602 - 0.8719) \times 10^3 \ Pa}{(30 \times 0.05 + 1000 \times 0.003 + 200 \times 0.25) \times 10^9 \ Ns/kg}$$

$$= 0.011 \times 10^{-6} \ kg/m^2s$$

C3.2.2   Heat loss

To calculate the heat loss, the U-value of the structure is required. There are strict guidelines, relating to heated buildings, set out in the Building Regulations Approved Document L, 1995 edition, to which the composite structure must adhere regarding permissible U-values for an external basement wall. The U-value must not, in such cases, be greater than 0.45 W/m²K.

(a)   U-value for wall

As for example C3.1.2; $U = 0.983 \ W/m^2K$

(b)   U-value for floor

$$U = \frac{1}{0.12 + \dfrac{0.05}{0.2} + \dfrac{0.003}{0.22} + \dfrac{0.25}{0.44} + 0.12}$$

$$= \frac{1}{1.0718} = 0.933 \ W/m^2K$$

C3.3   Type A protection: masonry construction, Grade 1 basement e.g. car park

This example demonstrates the calculations necessary for moisture and thermal transmittance through the masonry wall in the basement car park shown in Figure C5.

> **N.B. Negative values indicate moisture movement into the basement.**

C3.3.1   Moisture loss

(a)   Moisture loss through wall

Summer	P_{vi}	= 1.641 kPa	Winter P_{vi} = 0.6108 kPa
	P_{vo}	= 0.8719 kPa	
	G	= 20.3 GNs/kg	

where:

masonry	$r_1 = 35,$	$d_1 = 0.14$
mortar	$r_2 = 100,$	$d_2 = 0.075$
masonry	$r_3 = 35,$	$d_3 = 0.14$
vapour barrier	$r_4 = 1000,$	$d_4 = 0.003$

$$\text{Summer } M = \frac{(1.641 - 0.8719) \times 10^3 \ Pa}{(35 \times 0.14 + 100 \times 0.075 + 35 \times 0.14 + 1000 \times 0.003) \times 10^9 \ Ns/kg}$$

$$= \frac{0.7691 \times 10^3}{20.3 \times 10^9} = 0.0378 \times 10^{-6} \ kg/m^2s$$

$$\text{Winter } M = \frac{(0.6108 - 0.8719) \times 10^3}{20.3 \times 10^9} = -0.013 \times 10^{-6} \ kg/m^2s$$

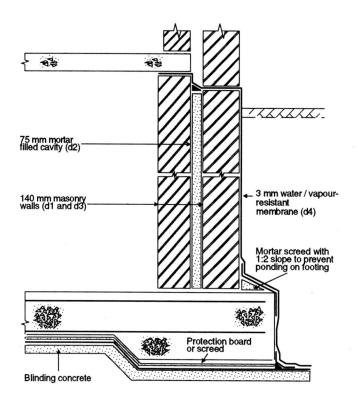

75 mm mortar filled cavity (d2)

140 mm masonry walls (d1 and d3)

3 mm water / vapour-resistant membrane (d4)

Mortar screed with 1:2 slope to prevent ponding on footing

Protection board or screed

Blinding concrete

Figure C5 Schematic section through Type A protection (masonry and external membrane) assumed in example calculation for moisture and thermal transmittance Grade 1 use - Car park (Floor details as for Figure C4)

C3.3.2 Heat loss

$$U = \frac{1}{(0.12 + \dfrac{0.14}{0.51} + \dfrac{0.075}{0.5} + \dfrac{0.14}{0.51} + \dfrac{0.003}{0.22} + 0.12)}$$

$$= \frac{1}{0.952}$$

$$= 1.05 \ W/m^2K$$

C3.4 Type B protection: concrete construction, Grade 1 basement e.g. car park

This example demonstrates the calculations necessary for moisture and thermal transmittance in the reinforced concrete walls and floor of the basement car park shown in Figure C6.

N.B. Negative values indicate moisture movement <u>into</u> the basement.

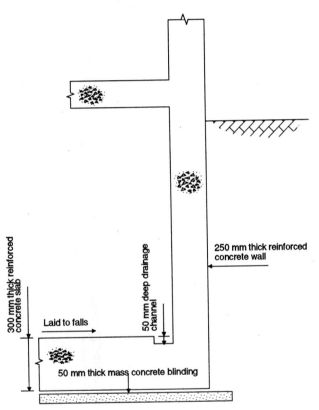

Figure C6 Schematic section through Type B protection (reinforced concrete box) assumed in example calculation for moisture and thermal transmittance Grade 1 use - Car park

C3.4.1 Moisture loss

(a)   Moisture loss through wall

$$\textbf{\textit{Summer M}} = \frac{(1.641 - 0.8719) \; x \; 10^3 \; \textit{Pa}}{(80 \; x \; 0.25) \; x \; 10^9 \; \textit{Ns/kg}}$$

$$= 0.038 \; x \; 10^6 \; \textit{kg/m²s}$$

$$\textbf{\textit{Winter}} = -0.013 \; x \; 10^6 \; \textit{kg/m²s}$$

(b)   Moisture loss through floor

$$\textbf{\textit{Summer M}} = \frac{(1.641 - 0.8719) \times 10^3 \; \textit{Pa}}{(30 \times 0.05 + 80 \times 0.3) \times 10^9 \; \textit{Ns/kg}}$$

$$= 0.03 \times 10^{-6} \; \textit{kg/m}^2 \; s$$

$$\textbf{\textit{Winter M}} = -0.01 \times 10^{-6} \; \textit{kg/m}^2 \; s$$

C3.4.2 Heat loss

(a)   U-value for wall

$$U = \frac{1}{0.12 + 0.568 + 0.12} = \frac{1}{0.806}$$

$$= 1.24 \; \textit{W/m²K}$$

(b)   U-value for floor

$$U = \frac{1}{0.12 + 0.25 + 0.682 + 0.12} = \frac{1}{1.172}$$

$$= 0.853 \; \textit{W/m}^2\textit{K}$$

C3.5 Type C protection: concrete construction, Grade 3 basement e.g. residential/office

This example demonstrates the calculations necessary for moisture and thermal transmittance through the reinforced concrete and drained cavity walls and floor in the basement used for residential or office accommodation shown in Figure C7.

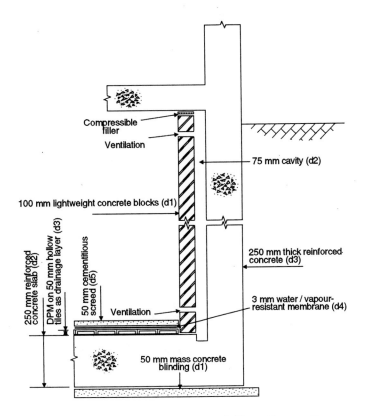

Figure C7 Schematic section through Type C protection (reinforced concrete and drained cavity wall) assumed in example calculation for moisture and thermal transmittance Grade 3 use - Residential / Office

---

N.B. The values selected for R and r for the cavity in this example assume that still air conditions prevail. Air movement in the cavity, either by natural or forced ventilation, would require the use of different values for these parameters. Where moving air conditions are expected, a building services engineer should be consulted.

Negative values indicate moisture movement <u>into</u> the basement.

C3.5.1 Moisture loss

(a) Moisture loss through wall

P_{vi} @ 24 °C Db and 60% RH = 1.811 kPa
P_{vo} @ 5 °C Db and 100% RH = 0.8719 kPa
G = 24.4 GNs/kg

where:

lightweight concrete	$r_1 = 40$, $d_1 = 0.1$
cavity	$r_2 = 5$, $d_2 = 0.075$
concrete	$r_3 = 80$, $d_3 = 0.25$

$$M = \frac{(1.811 - 0.8719) \times 10^3 \; Pa}{(40 \times 0.1 + 5 \times 0.075 + 80 \times 0.25) \times 10^9 \; Ns/kg}$$

$$= \frac{0.9391 \times 10^3 \; N/m^2}{24.4 \times 10^9 \; Ns/kg}$$

$$= 0.038 \times 10^{-6} \; kg/m^2s$$

(b)   Moisture loss through floor

$P_{vi} = 1.811$ kPa
$P_{vo} = 0.8719$ kPa
$G = 35$ GNs/kg

where:

concrete blinding	$r_1 = 30,$	$d_1 = 0.05$
concrete	$r_2 = 80,$	$d_2 = 0.25$
hollow tiles	$r_3 = 10,$	$d_3 = 0.05$
water-resistant	$r_4 = 1000,$	$d_4 = 0.003$
screed	$r_5 = 200,$	$d_5 = 0.05$

$$M = \frac{0.9391 \times 10^3}{35 \times 10^9}$$

$$= 0.026 \times 10^{-6} \; kg/m^2s$$

C3.5.2   *Heat loss*

(a)   U-value for walls

$$U = \frac{1}{(0.12 + 0.53 + 0.17 + 0.57 + 0.12)} = \frac{1}{1.51} = 0.66 \; W/m^2K$$

(b)   U-value for floor

$$U = \frac{1}{(0.12 + 0.25 + 0.57 + 0.5 + 0.013 + 0.122 + 0.12)} = \frac{1}{1.695} = 0.59 \; W/m^2K$$

As the moisture transfer rate is very small, it is suggested that the conditions are assumed to exist for 60 days. Hence to obtain the total moisture transfer over this period in kg/m² the calculated rate has to be multiplied by 5.184×10^6 seconds to obtain the final figure.

C4   CALCULATION OF INSULATION REQUIREMENTS

In all the examples, the calculated U-value did not meet the Building Regulations required maximum of 0.45 W/m²K for the composite structure. In order to comply with this requirement, a number of options are available. The installation of a layer of insulating material will improve the structural thermal properties:

$$U = \frac{1}{R} \quad and \quad U = 0.45 \ or \ less, \quad hence \ R = 2.22 \ or \ more$$

Referring to Section C3.1.2, $R = 1.017$; therefore the additional R value required from insulation can be determined by

$$R_{insul} = 2.22 - 1.017 = 1.203$$

Select phenolic foam with a density of 30 kg/m² and a thermal conductivity of 0.04.

The thickness of insulation required:

$$= 1.203 \times 0.04 = 0.048 \ m$$

Hence a 50 mm slab of phenolic foam insulation will bring this wall into compliance with the Building Regulations.

With the layer of insulation installed within the structure, not only are the thermal properties improved, but the moisture transfer through the structure is also reduced.

In the above example, if a 50 mm thick layer of insulation provided then the surface vapour resistance G becomes

$$G = 28 + (500 \times 0.05)$$
$$= 53 \times 10^9 \ Ns/kg$$

$$and \ hence \ M = 0.0145 \times 10^{-6} \ kg/m^2s$$

i.e. it reduces the moisture transfer by nearly 50%.

Failure to comply with the U-value set down by the Building Regulations may result in an uncomfortable and undesirable environment within the basement. This may result in complaints from building users. Better insulation may reduce 'wetness' problems.